VOLUME ONE

HEALTH PLANNING IN THE UNITED STATES:

Selected Policy Issues

Committee on Health Planning Goals and Standards

Institute of Medicine

NATIONAL ACADEMY PRESS
Washington, D.C.   1981

NOTICE   The project that is the subject of this report was approved by the Governing Board of the National Research Council, whose members are drawn from the Councils of the National Academy of Sciences, the National Academy of Engineering, and the Institute of Medicine. The members of the committee responsible for the report were chosen for their special competencies and with regard for appropriate balance.

    This report has been reviewed by a group other than the authors according to procedures approved by a Report Review Committee consisting of members of the National Academy of Sciences, the National Academy of Engineering, and the Institute of Medicine.

The Institute of Medicine was chartered in 1970 by the National Academy of Sciences to enlist distinguished members of the appropriate professions in the examination of policy matters pertaining to the health of the public. In this, the Institute acts under both the Academy's 1863 congressional charter responsibility to be an advisor to the federal government and its own initiative in identifying issues of medical care, research, and education.

Supported by the Health Resources Administration Contract No. 282-78-0163-EJM

LIBRARY OF CONGRESS CATALOGING IN PUBLICATION DATA
National Academy of Sciences (U.S.). Institute of
    Medicine. Committee on Health Planning Goals
    and Standards.
    Health planning in the United States.

    Bibliography: v. 1, p.
    1. Health planning—United States. 2. Medical
policy—United States. I. Title. [DNLM: 1. Health
planning—United States. WA 540 AA1 H227]
RA395.A3N285 1981   362.1:06   81-9534
ISBN 0-309-03144-3 (v.1)   AACR2

Available from

NATIONAL ACADEMY PRESS
2101 Constitution Ave., N.W.
Washington, D.C. 20418

Printed in the United States of America

COMMITTEE ON
HEALTH PLANNING GOALS
AND STANDARDS

RASHI FEIN, Professor, Economics of Medicine, Harvard
   Medical School, *Chairman*

ROBERT A. DERZON, Vice-President, Lewin & Associates, Inc.
HENRY A. DiPRETE, Vice-President, John Hancock Mutual
   Life Insurance Company
JEAN L. HARRIS, Secretary of Human Resources, Commonwealth
   of Virginia
JOHN K. IGLEHART, Vice-President, Kaiser Foundation Health
   Plan
JAMES R. KIMMEY, Executive Director, Institute for Health
   Planning
BEN R. LAWTON, President, Marshfield Clinic
ROSLYN LINDHEIM, Professor of Architecture, University
   of California
THEODORE MARMOR, Chairman, Center for Health Studies,
   Yale University
WALTER J. McNERNEY, President, Blue Cross and Blue
   Shield Associations
ANTHONY MOTT, Executive Director, Finger Lake Health
   Systems Agency
NORA PIORE, Senior Program Consultant, The Commonwealth
   Fund
WILLIAM C. RICHARDSON, Professor and Associate Dean,
   University of Washington
BRUCE C. VLADECK, Assistant Commissioner of Health,
   State of New Jersey

LIAISON MEMBERS FROM THE NATIONAL COUNCIL ON HEALTH
PLANNING AND DEVELOPMENT

S. PHILIP CAPER, Vice-Chancellor for Health Affairs and
   Professor of Medicine, University of Massachusetts
   Medical Center
L. EMMERSON WARD, Professor of Medicine, Mayo Medical
   School

STAFF

HELEN DARLING, *Study Director*
DOROTHY S. POOLE, *Research Associate*
MARYANNE CUNNINGHAM, *Secretary*
JESSICA TOWNSEND, *Consultant*

COMMISSIONED PAPERS

LAWRENCE BROWN, The Brookings Institution
BARRY CHECKOWAY, University of Illinois at Urbana
DONALD COHODES, Johns Hopkins University
GEORGE DOWNS, University of California at Davis
DOROTHY ELLENBURG, The Coalition for Effective Human
   Services
JAMES MORONE, University of Chicago
GREGORY RAAB, Health Care Financing Administration
HARVEY SAPOLSKY, Massachusetts Institute of Technology

PREFACE

In the few months since the Committee on Health Planning Goals and Standards met for the last time, there have been substantial changes in the leadership of our country. There is a new President. There will be new administrators of the program with which this report is concerned, and there are changes in the composition and power centers of the Congress that will reevaluate and determine the future of the health planning program. These events increase the importance of this document. Certainly the timing is fortuitous as task forces and individuals, yet unburdened by previous policies and commitments, cast a fresh eye on a variety of national policies.

The health planning effort, though quite modest by any standard except local citizen involvement, is a particularly vulnerable government program. First, its funds are not tied to any entitlement program. Its elimination thus would give the appearance of saving money. Second, because it is a compromise program of many interests and values in the health sector, it has no natural or defined constituency. Third, while its planning mission is carried out locally by a citizen-dominated local advisory mechanism, the mission and its goals are poorly understood, especially in Washington. Understanding of that mission was not enhanced by the executive branch's efforts to redefine the program into one that was expected to carry out the federal government's desire for "cost containment" and efforts to reduce the number of hospital beds. Since some of the major recommendations of this report are aimed at helping to sort out some of the misunderstandings and unrealistic expectations of the planning program, and explaining about its unusual local citizen-controlled structure for advising on health investments, the committee and I hope that those charged with responsibility for reviewing and implementing the health planning act will read this report and the commissioned papers with care.

This IOM document was produced by a group of citizens who gave their time and effort because of their concern about health care and the problems that health planning is aimed at ameliorating, in particular, and about government programs in general.

This preface is written by the chairman. Let me state my perspective on the work of the committee. We did not view our charge as listed on page two in narrow terms. We did not limit our inquiry to ways in which the health planning program might be improved. Rather, we began at an earlier stage discussing the rationale for health planning, asking how the program should be judged, whether it can measure up to that which some expect of it, and whether its realized and potential benefits justify its costs. I believe we started with a premise: that government programs should not be supported simply because their goals were worthy or condemned simply because they used nonmarket decision-making mechanisms. We concluded that, by itself, the health planning effort, as constituted or even with the improvements we recommended, could not accomplish what some desired of it: significant control of health care costs. The cost containment rationale for planning and regulation has assumed greater importance in the years since the enactment of the original legislation and has been used, primarily in Washington, as the criterion by which to assess the performance of health planning. The committee believes that the forces at work in the American health care system, including the various reimbursement mechanisms, cannot be countered by a health planning effort that is divorced, among other limiting factors, from the flow of funds.

To expect more of health planning than it can possibly deliver is unfair and not only to those who work hard to make health planning work. It is unfair to all those Americans whose expectations are aroused, and whose hopes subsequently are dashed. It may be convenient to "oversell" in order to enact and renew legislation and to pass appropriation measures, but such overselling is harmful in the long run. There is a day of reckoning, and in that day of reckoning, the program in question loses its supporters. Yet even more than that occurs: the public grows cynical, feels it has been duped, and loses faith in its institutions.

If setting criteria that guarantee disappointment is irresponsible and damaging to public confidence and trust in government leadership and government programs--it would be similarly irresponsible for this committee not to set forth criteria that it believes are appropriate. We have stated that, by itself, health planning cannot serve as a major cost containment program. But we have gone further. We asked: "What can an effective health planning program accomplish?" and "Are those objectives worth the effort?" We concluded that the health planning activity can make a number of important contributions. Health planning can bring existing disparities in access to our attention and can help plan for a more equitable distribution of services. It can assist in the attainment of a more effective and efficient health care system and thus contribute to cost containment. Containing costs through increased system efficiency--not by denying care to persons who need and can benefit from care or by arbitrary cost cutting or budget cuts that reduce services that have long run benefits--is an objective worth pursuing.

Furthermore, health planning can contribute to other objectives that this committee believes are important. These objectives reflect our faith in the value inherent in giving voice to those whose needs cannot be adequately articulated through political or economic power. The health care system touches every American, and health planning provides an opportunity for many who would otherwise be left out to express their concerns and priorities.

Does the contribution that health planning makes and can make to the attainment of those objectives justify the effort? This committee is convinced that the answer to that question is yes. We do not reach that conclusion simply because of our admiration for the thousands of individuals in communities across the country who, on a volunteer basis, have given of their time to make health planning work--though we do note the fact that so many have done so, and continue to do so, is not an irrelevant datum. Nor did we reach this conclusion simply because there is evidence that, in some areas, health planning has made a contribution to the rationalization of resources. That datum, too, is important. Nonetheless, it is an insufficient rationale for a federal program that is national in scope. Our conclusion that the health planning effort is justified was reached on the basis of a careful review of the papers contributed by our consultants, on the basis of our own reviews and discussions and experience. Our assessment is not as quantitative as some would like it to be. We are aware of this "shortcoming." We believe, however, that this is in the nature of the program. Much of what it can accomplish involves the democratic process, the creation of an informed citizenry and changes in the climate of opinion. At this point in the history of the program, the program will have to be monitored and assessed for understanding, improvements, and insights, rather than evaluated in a rigorous scientific manner.

But while the program should be sustained, that does not mean it cannot be improved upon. We offer some specific recommendations of ways by which program performance could be improved in the two areas that we examined closely. The reader will note that many of the recommendations call for greater flexibility. The committee is convinced that the health planning effort is complex and that it is necessary to cast many of its activities in a quasi-experimental mode. There is little reason to believe that present arrangements necessarily are optimal or that arrangements that are effective in one area or region will necessarily be effective elsewhere. Our statement that we favor flexibility and experimentation has a corollary: that a purposeful effort be made to learn from these various experiments, from these differences. Unless the various experiments and the research concerning them are planned, we will not maximize the knowledge gained and will be only slightly better off in the future than we are today.

Finally, it is important to note that the committee has concluded that, if health planning is to succeed, it is necessary that those volunteers and staff people in Washington and in all 50 states be given a period of fiscal and temporal stability in which they are permitted to do their jobs. No program can succeed if it is constantly subjected to changing guidelines, altered priorities, and mixed signals. Nor is morale enhanced if the program and the required appropriations are constantly in jeopardy. It is possible to ensure failure by underfunding programs, harassing administrators, showing little appreciation for the thousands of citizens involved, and setting unattainable goals. It is also possible to foster a perception that government does not work and leaders cannot lead if those who enact legislation fail to support it and if those who oppose it, having lost, continue to try to scuttle activities. Whatever one's views are on the appropriate role for government and the private sector, surely all agree that it is unhealthy for the body politic to ask people to do a job and then create situations that make it impossible for them to succeed.

The reader should note that all of the above is in the preface. Perhaps all of my colleagues on the committee agree with what I have written, but the tone and the exact wording should not be ascribed to my colleagues. One of the privileges a chairman has is to write the preface. I have tried to sum up my thoughts as they developed during the committee work. The committee document, however, does not rest on my ideas or on my formulation, and it is the committee document that is important and that should be reviewed and considered.

I know, however, that I speak for all members of the committee when I express our deep thanks to all those who worked so very hard to produce this report on time. We especially thank Helen Darling. Few committees have had as able a study director. The laws of probability ensure that that is the case because there are few study directors as able as Helen Darling. All that I said about her in our first report still holds true. Our second year together underlines that which we noted then. I know that if I am again asked to serve as chairman of an IOM committee, my first question will be: Who is the study director? I suspect that is the question my colleagues will also ask.

Thanks are due as well to David Hamburg, who was President of the IOM during almost all of the life of this study, and Frederick Robbins, the current President. Karl Yordy, William Lybrand, and Carleton Evans have provided continuing administrative support that has made it possible for the staff to concentrate on the study. In addition, throughout the 2 years of this study we have enjoyed the strong encouragement and cooperation of key officials in the Health Resources Administration, including Henry Foley, formerly Administrator. Dr. Foley's personal support and interest from the study's inception have been gratifying. Special thanks are due to Laurel Shannon, who has been an able and committed project officer throughout the life of the study. More recently, James Stockdill and Iris Schneider have assisted us in reviews by the program's federal administrators.

In addition to the authors who contributed papers, I would also like to recognize the assistance of many people too numerous to name who have given freely of their advice, critical reviews and assistance over the past 2 years. In particular, Dan Zwick, Harry Cain, Robert Sigmond, and Katherine Bauer have reviewed different parts of the report and their comments have been appreciated.

Finally, as chairman, I want to thank all committee members. As in the first year of the committee's life, they made my task most pleasant and stimulating. When we began we were members of a committee, when we concluded, after 2 years together, we were friends. My thanks to them for making what might have been a chore a rewarding activity.

Rashi Fein
Chairman

CONTENTS

1 INTRODUCTION

For the past 2 years, a committee of the Institute of
Medicine has examined policy issues related to the
nation's current health planning program, at the request
of the Health Resources Administration, in the U.S.
Department of Health and Human Services (DHHS). This
volume covers the committee's work in the second year
of the study on two important, timely issues: national,
state, and local roles and relationships in health
planning and the participation of "consumers"* in the
advisory roles given to the planning agencies.

A previous volume, *Health Planning in the United
States: Issues in Guideline Development* (Institute of
Medicine, 1980), dealt with policy questions related
directly to the development of national health planning
goals and standards, and described a theoretical framework for examining the health planning program. The
first volume reviewed the literature and the history of
health planning in the United States.

At the end of its first year's work, the committee
made specific recommendations to the Health Resources
Administration on the possible use of national health
planning guidelines as instruments for the establishment
and promulgation of public policy. The committee observed that in a heterogeneous society that values the
collaborative, bargaining mode of policymaking, the
process of creating guidelines is itself important. The

---

*The language of P.L. 93-641 stipulates consumers, con-
sumer majority, and consumer participation, but means lay
citizens. The terms reflect the distinction between "providers" of health care and their opposites, "consumers."

committee asserted that the guidelines should: (a) result from a systematic and highly participatory process; (b) be on as firm an empirical base as possible; (c) be disseminated with relevant documentation; and (d) be developed with advisories on agenda setting and priorities from the National Council on Health Planning and Development. The council should, it was concluded, be given an expanded and strengthened role.

The Health Resources Administration (HRA) then requested that the Institute of Medicine committee spend another year analyzing problems related to consumer involvement and intergovernmental and private agency relationships. Their request was made partly on the basis of the urgency of some of the policy issues and HRA's desire for advice from an independent institution on those particularly important, thorny subjects.

Although the focus of the study in the second year is on those two broad issues, the committee found it impossible to talk about effective consumer participation or productive national, state, and local relationships without some agreement on the purposes of the health planning program, and a vision of what would be considered an effective program or an effective participant in it. This report, therefore, also contains a discussion of the committee's perspective on the entire program.

The charge to the committee in the second year was (1) to identify issues in national, state, and local roles and relationships and consumer participation that affect the health planning program; (2) to discuss alternative approaches to a more effective program; and (3) to make specific recommendations or comments concerning the issues raised.

In the second year, the committee's objectives included the following: (1) to clarify the issues and expand the knowledge base, thus assisting the Health Resources Administration in preparing, retaining, and revising policies and guidelines on consumer participation and national, state, and local relationships in health planning; (2) to assist Health Systems Agencies, Statewide Health Coordinating Councils, and State Health Planning and Development Agencies in fostering the most effective linkages with each other and other agencies; (3) to identify sources of tension that negatively affect the program and make recommendations for their amelioration; and (4) to improve the theoretical and

empirical foundations for understanding health planning
and regulation.

ACTIVITIES

In the second year, the committee conducted a review of
the literature, held public hearings, and commissioned
10 background papers. The pertinent literature on health
planning and regulation was selectively examined with particular attention to studies of consumer participation
and national, state, and local relationships.

Early in the second year of the study, March 27, 1980,
a public hearing was held at the National Academy of
Sciences.* More than 600 persons and organizations were
invited to present their testimony to the committee, based
on a list of questions on which the committee was seeking
advice. A roster of those who submitted written statements
to the committee is given in the Appendix.

The committee was particularly interested in the
positions of representative organizations of consumers,
public interest groups, and public officials. Their
participation was actively sought, and many presented
testimony.

The committee also commissioned 10 papers on aspects
of the study. The papers and the authors are: Lawrence D.
Brown--"Structural Issues in National, State, and Local
Relations in Health Planning"; Barry Checkoway--"Consumer-
ism in Health Planning Agencies" and "Consumer Movements
in Health Planning"; Donald Cohodes--"Interstate Varia-
tion in Certificate-of-Need Programs--A Review and
Prospectus"; George Downs--"Monitoring the Health Planning
System: Data, Measurement and Inference Problems";
Dorothy Ellenburg--"Special Interests Versus Citizen Control: Who Owns Planning?"; James A. Morone--"The Real
World of Representation: Consumers and the HSAs" and
"Models of Representation: Consumers and the HSAs"; G.
Gregody Raab--"National, State, and Local Relationships
in Health Planning: Interest Group Reaction and Lobbying";
and Harvey Sapolsky--"Bottoms Up is Upside Down." They
constitute Volume Two of this report and are referenced
simply by authors' names in this volume.

---

*This was actually the committee's second public hearing.
The first (March 1979) was concerned primarily with the
national health planning goals and standards.

Impressions from health planners working in agencies throughout the country were garnered from a discussion arranged by two committee members, at the Annual Meeting of the American Health Planning Association. More than 30 planning agency board members and planners participated. The committee met five times in this second study period. In addition, two groups of authors met with representatives of the committee to discuss the papers at an early stage. The authors also met for a 1-day session with the full committee before the preparation of the committee's recommendations.

As in the first year, the committee and staff visited health planning agencies, met with governing body members and staff, routinely reviewed agency reports, Health Systems Plans, and attended selected training activities.

ORGANIZATION OF THE REPORT

This report has two volumes. Volume One, the committee's policy statement, has five chapters. Chapter 2 provides a short overview of the health planning program. It discusses some of the general issues concerning topics covered in detail in Chapters 3 and 4, and provides background information on the purposes of the health planning program and approaches to assessing its effectiveness. Chapter 3 contains the committee's findings and recommendations concerning national, state, and local relations in health planning. Chapter 4 has the committee's observations and recommendations on consumer participation. Chapter 5 is a summary of key findings and the recommendations.

Volume Two is composed of the background papers commissioned by the committee. They detail the empirical and theoretical underpinnings of the study. The authors were encouraged to express their opinions and make their own recommendations. The papers, although reviewed by the Academy, are not submitted to the same review process as committee reports and represent the views of the individual authors, not the committee or the Institute of Medicine. The committee feels that the papers by themselves constitute major contributions to the quality of current debates in health planning and should be disseminated broadly.

2 SELECTED ISSUES IN HEALTH PLANNING

This chapter first summarizes some of the committee's principal concerns about limitations of the nation's health planning program. It then presents selected background information on the program and an overview of some pressing policy questions. Particular attention is paid to issues of national, state, and local relations and of consumer participation. The chapter concludes with a discussion of the purposes of the health planning program and what the committee believes to be reasonable expectations for it.

In general, the health planning program in the United States may be characterized as a citizen-dominated trusteeship in the field of health. At its best and at its most inspiring theoretical level, it may be seen as a new institution charged with helping to ensure that individual institutions or actors will promote, or at least not adversely affect, the development of a health care system that provides for all the citizenry, "access to quality health care at reasonable cost."* In many places, there are literally hundreds of interested and committed volunteers trying to make it work. Like all of our social institutions, when operating and viewed up close, the picture is sometimes less inspiring, and suffers from human failures. As always, there are problems in devising arrangements and methods for structuring the unusual American institution that is health planning, but the committee believes that the effort is worthwhile, as stated in its first year's report. In particular, the

---

*It is both a goal and an explicit assumption of this act that citizens should have access to needed health services without regard to socioeconomic status.

committee wishes to encourage much more flexibility in
administration and, where local communities desire it,
experimentation. The intentionally decentralized process
for planning and resources development should be viewed
as an opportunity for learning how to help deploy health
resources in this country.

The National Health Planning and Resources Development
Act of 1974 (Public Law 93-641) was intended to establish
the structure and support for health planning. The agencies established under the law were to ensure a systematic
development of resources, especially new technology.
Local level planning was to be conducted by Health Systems
Agencies (HSAs), governed by local citizens on a board
having a "consumer" majority.* The act was to link health
planning more closely to decisions about the allocation
of health care resources, by having local HSAs advise
public and private decision-makers about the needs and
priorities of an area for health programs and services.
The law also was designed to encourage institutions and
programs to bring their own planning in line with the
area's perceived priorities for services, recognizing
that most "health planning" is done by those who deliver
services.

The local-state-national planning network initiated by
P.L. 93-641 was viewed by some of its supporters as only
one piece of a larger, more comprehensive strategy of
controls and new financing mechanisms in the health system. But a principal legislative component of that
strategy--national health insurance--was not passed by
the Congress. Some other pieces of the health system's
intended refurbishment, such as Professional Standards
Review Organizations and Health Maintenance Organization
legislation, were enacted, but the planning structure
never became as fully buttressed as many of its architects
had hoped.

The health planning agencies were intended to encourage a more effective health system overall, which would
reduce inefficiencies and, therefore, indirectly control

------

*Under the law a distinction is made between "consumers"
and "providers" of health care services. For the most
part, consumers are lay citizens who do not have a policymaking or fiduciary role in health institutions. For a
more detailed definition of a consumer, see Chapter 4.

costs. Institutions would be urged to mesh their plans with needs in the area; technical assistance would be provided to community agencies and organizations in shaping their programs; plans and projects would be developed to improve the community's health care system; and federal projects would be made consistent with local needs and preferences.

The planning program was not intended to be a major cost containment device, and it lacks the authority needed to control expenditures. But with the likelihood of a national health insurance program fading and little promise of a cost containment bill making it through the Congress in the late 1970s, the cost containment potential of the health planning structure received increasing emphasis by its federal administrators.

The HSAs' authority as exercised indirectly through state certificate-of-need programs or appropriateness review was seen as a strategy for cost control. But the authority that really could have strengthened the cost containment capability of the agencies--such as direct linkages to existing reimbursement mechanisms, limits on total allowable capital investment, or mandatory rate control programs--was not granted. There is little question that in 1974 Congress did not intend that health planning agencies would set strict limits on resources. Further, it has not yet enacted a more direct approach to control through a capital expenditures limit.

In the structure of the health planning system, the only intersection of planning responsibilities with financial liability is in state governors' offices. State Medicaid expenditures are among the fastest growing and most politically sensitive of all state budgetary items, yet the health planning program, at both state and federal levels, has never fully recognized this possible convergence of interests. In part, that lack of recognition comes from the fact that Medicaid is built administratively on welfare programs, not health, and the health planning structure incorporated earlier activities that had largely been the responsibility of state health departments. Also, federal officials in the public health service have never had a very clear understanding of the political dynamics of Medicaid in the states. However, the relatively brief experience with the planning law suggests that concern about Medicaid expenditures can make a state desire to operate an aggressive planning program and, as Cohodes in Volume Two suggests, such political "will" is vital to its success. In addition, the role of the states was relatively weak because the congressional authors of P.L. 93-641 feared that governors would be narrowly interested in minimizing Medicaid costs, to the possible detriment of the health system as a whole.

Built-in limitations on effectiveness of the planning program are sometimes overlooked by critics who emphasize the wide-ranging mandate written in the law. Even now, naive expectations persist about what is possible for the health planning network. It was assigned lofty, laudable, but difficult goals--to assist in "the achievement of equal access to quality health care at a reasonable cost." It was intentionally deprived of any real budgetary or regulatory powers by which to accomplish these goals. It was asked to focus on objectives that are sometimes seen as contradictory, such as improving health status and controlling costs. There is a need to find feasible measures of effectiveness against which the planning program can be judged, and this committee discusses its approach at the end of this chapter. Previous studies evaluated only the extent to which certificate-of-need activities decreased capital expenditures--ignoring the role of Certificate of Need (CON) as an allocator of resources--and treated them as a uniform national program. However, CON is a state program and varies greatly across the nation (see Cohodes' paper). Further, other aspects of planning are worthy of evaluation.

As is often the case in U.S. politics, a crisis atmosphere and inflated promises accompanied the passage of the planning act. Unrealistic adherence to such elevated expectations virtually ensures that a program will be viewed as unsuccessful no matter what it accomplishes. *The committee believes that there is a need to scaledown the unrealistic expectations for the health planning program.* The political process seems to require rhetoric and overselling in order to maintain a coalition, but the committee feels that the effect of the overselling is not neutral; it fosters skepticism about our nation's ability to solve problems and discourages faith in any government action.

The Health Systems Agencies are the basic units of a complex, locally directed system for determining a community's health resource needs and for advising governmental and other decision-makers about those determinations. The planning system should be viewed as an important, somewhat experimental, effort toward forming relationships among agencies of government, between the public and private sectors, and between the processes of politics and technology. The HSAs should be evaluated as to whether they fulfill criteria of a democratic process, including fairness, openness, potential for participation, and extent to which they employ data and information appropriately. The committee is not suggesting that process considerations form the sole basis for program evaluation. The priorities for the planning program set forth in the enabling legislation suggest that Congress had definite ideas about the outcomes of the process. A variety of "ends" were defined in the congressional priorities. Those "ends" may not be the sole justification for the "means" or the process, but neither do the "means" stand alone. Congress clearly hoped that promoting and facilitating a community-based planning process would contribute to improvements in health status and the health system, including cost-containing improvements. These desired improvements affect our judgment of the process and provide further evaluation criteria for assessment of the act and the programs created under its provisions.* In the final analysis, expectations of the planning agency network, and of the degree to which generalizations can be made concerning its "success," must remain modest and sensible, geared to the scale, nature, and actual power of the program. Evaluators should remember that inefficiencies and frustrations are inherent in the planning program as in Congress or other legislative bodies. To judge the program by theoretical standards of rational decision-making would be inappropriate.

BACKGROUND

The National Health Planning and Resources Development Act of 1974 (Public Law 93-641) was an evolutionary step in the development of health planning in the United

---

*Health Systems Plans, developed by HSAs, indicate community concerns. Cost containment is only one issue addressed by plan documents. A 1978 survey of 146 HSA first-year plans found that 92 percent recommended a health promotion component, and over half of these agencies were working with outside groups to encourage health promotion activities.

States, not a revolutionary break with previous practice. The Congress built on existing voluntary and government-sponsored activities in designing the local, state, federal, private, and public arrangement that makes up the bulk of the current health planning system.

Before passing the 1974 act, Congress reviewed several earlier health planning and resource development initiatives and found them wanting. Existing areawide and state comprehensive health planning agencies were judged lacking in ability to implement their plans. Resource development programs, such as the Regional Medical Programs, the Experimental Health Services Delivery Systems, and the Hill-Burton facilities construction activities, were seen as excessively fragmented and isolated from community planning efforts. In merging these existing federal interests in planning and resources development into a single program, Congress anticipated a system in which the flow of resources would follow plans developed at the local level and be incorporated into state planning efforts.

A regulatory activity--certificate of need--was added to implement decisions and moderate the flow of capital into the health industry. In addition to provisions affecting the local and state levels, Congress called for the development of a national health planning policy to guide the development of health resources throughout the nation (particularly medical facilities and new technology) and assist in setting priorities for federal health program investments.

Congress concluded that the massive infusion of federal funds into the health care system following enactment of Medicare and Medicaid had been inflationary. Yet, the increased health expenditures failed to produce an adequate supply or distribution of resources. There still were problems of access to needed health care, quality of care, and availability of services. Instances were identified in which substantial numbers of citizens had not fully shared in the benefits of social and medical progress. In the planning legislation, Congress reaffirmed the national commitment to provide quality, affordable, health care to meet the needs of all citizens, and also put a high priority on dampening health care costs.

The major structural and procedural characteristics of the program are firmly rooted in important political and social realities. These include the incremental nature of policymaking, the careful preservation of private and public roles, and belief in the importance (both as a value and a technical necessity) of having local-level, extragovernmental organizations advising those with decision-making responsibilities. In turn, those with the power of decision, for example, the states, have elaborate due process and administrative procedural requirements.

Health Systems Agencies (HSAs)

The act authorized and required the development of a nationwide network of local planning agencies, HSAs. Once health service areas were established, applications were sought from public or private, nonprofit entities that desired designation as the HSA for the area. Of the 203 agencies ultimately designated as HSAs by the Secretary of DHHS, 180 are private nonprofit agencies, while the remaining 23 are based either in public regional planning bodies or units of local government. Two hundred and eleven health service areas have been established, covering the entire area of the United States and its territories.*

Each HSA must have a governing body with a majority of its members defined as health care consumers rather than providers. The problems and opportunities related to consumer participation, including compositional issues, are detailed in Chapter 4.

The remainder of the members of the governing body are to represent health professions, health care institutions, insurers, educational programs for the health professions, allied health professions, and hospital administration. The membership of the governing body must also include, through its provider or consumer components, representation of general purpose local government, elected

---

*In 11 cases, because of geographic and demographic factors, the boundaries of a health service area are coterminous with those of a state. In 16 areas, the stipulation against subdivision of SMSAs, or other factors, led to the creation of interstate health service areas. The act exempted some jurisdictions from the requirement to designate HSAs. These areas are served by a state agency that also carries out HSA functions. These are called 1536 agencies.

officials, nonmetropolitan areas, and mental health
interests. If there is a Veterans Administration facility
or a health maintenance organization in the area, it also
must be represented.

The 1974 act did not specify a process for governing
body selection. The 1979 amendments required that the
process used to select governing body members meet mini-
mum statutory requirements concerning community participation in, and understanding of, the selection process. A
majority of the members must be selected in a manner that
is not "self-perpetuating." In a private nonprofit agency,
the governing body is responsible for managing the affairs
of the agency and for directing its various functions.
In a governmentally based HSA, the governing body's
responsibilities are more circumscribed, with the parent
governmental borad or council retaining key functions
regarding budgetary and personnel matters, as well as a
key role in the planning process.

The act, as amended in 1979, states five purposes for
the HSAs:

1. improving the health of residents of a health
service area;
2. increasing the accessibility, acceptability, con-
tinuity and quality of health services provided residents
of the area;
3. restraining increases in the cost of providing
residents with health services;
4. preventing unnecessary duplication of health
resources; and
5. preserving and improving competition in the health
service area.

Planning in the HSA

The process of developing area health services plans is
central to all other activities carried out by HSAs. The
agencies collect and analyze data concerning the health
status of the areas' residents and the health resources
available to them. With this description of existing
conditions, the HSA develops goals for the following 5
years, describing a desired state of community health and
health services. These goals, along with supporting objectives, recommended actions, and estimates of the
resources required to achieve its goals, are incorporated

into a Health Systems Plan (HSP). An annual plan of
action is prepared that outlines specific steps to be
taken that year toward achieving the HSP goals. This
Annual Implementation Plan (AIP) is intended to guide the
activities of those involved in the provision of health
services in a community. Representatives of a variety of
community interests participate in the process of
developing plans.

The 5-year plan (HSP) must be reviewed and updated at
least once every 3 years, although plan development and
update is a continuous process in most HSAs. These plans
are important as consensus documents stating a community's
health goals and describing the means to achieve them.
They form the basis for the HSA's recommendations and decisions concerning allocation of resources--the implementation function.

Each HSA is required to pursue organized efforts to
secure changes in its health service area that support
the goals of its plan. These implementation responsibilities include both planning and quasi-regulatory efforts.
The former consist of information gathering and analysis,
technical assistance and consultation with community
organizations and agencies, development of plans and
projects for achieving plan goals, and review and approval
of proposed uses of federal health funds in the area.
Quasi-regulatory activities include recommendations to
the state under the certificate-of-need program and the
review of the appropriateness of services offered in an
area.

Appropriateness Review

One of the more controversial agency activities is the
periodic review of health services to determine the
appropriateness of services offered to the needs of residents. Reducing a mismatch between current requirements
and services designed for an earlier time was seen as an
opportunity to reduce waste and inefficiency in the
system. Congress therefore required that planners look
at existing services to determine whether or not they
continue to meet current needs.

The HSA reports its findings concerning appropriateness to the State Health Planning Development Agency,
which in turn makes the findings public. There is no
sanction attached to a finding of inappropriateness, but

such findings must be accompanied by an HSA plan of
remedial actions that would correct the inappropriate
situation.

Appropriateness review was proposed late in the legislative process and there is very little information
available concerning congressional expectations of it.
Appropriateness review emerged as a last-minute substitute
for a section that would have required that all services
be periodically recertified. This was politically unacceptable at the time, but as a background it has led to
appropriateness review's being regarded as threatening
to many health care institutions. The lack of speci-
ficity about what it is, how it will be used, and how it
might be linked to future reimbursement or financing
have raised anxieties and efforts to secure its repeal.
But there was little interest in its removal in 1979 and
appropriateness reviews of selected services are now
under way.

Proposed Use of Federal Funds

Another congressional concern during the development of
the basic health planning legislation was the consistency
of federal health projects and contracts with local
goals and desires, as well as existing services. To
assure that targeted federal financial investments were
in line with local priorities, HSAs were given the authority to review and approve or disapprove proposed uses of
federal funds (PUFF) in their areas. Each application
for most federal funds from the Public Health Services
must be submitted to the HSA. Upon receipt of the
application, the HSA has 60 days in which to make a
decision. The HSA's comments on the proposal are sent
to the applicant, the relevant federal funding agency,
the state agency, and the state program. But federal
programs subject to this requirement represent a relatively small portion of the federal dollars flowing into a
community. For example, Medicare and Medicaid expenditures are excluded from review. Nevertheless, the funds
subject to review represent a significant amount of the
federal discretionary money in health.

The federal grant review function has evoked contro-
versy within the federal government. Many programs that
once distributed funds with relative freedom resent the
HSAs' authority to document and possibly override

federal judgment. This friction delayed the development of regulations and policies governing PUFF review and continues to create problems. Although the HSA has decision-making authority in this matter, the secretary can override a decision upon request of an applicant. Whether or not this authority is used frequently will depend in large part on the competence with which HSAs approach this responsibility.* In addition to the federal tensions, there are sometimes conflicts at the local level. Many of the funds that come under review are categorical grant programs that serve special groups, most often the traditionally underserved and politically weak. Further, medical researchers feel it is inappropriate for local health planning bodies to review their funding applications.

Certificate of Need and 1122 Review--HSA

One of the major implementation tools given planning agencies is the review of proposed institutional capital spending. The HSA recommends to the state agency approval or disapproval of applications for capital expenditures. The HSA's determination of need should be based on analysis of data and community desires as expressed in planning documents. Review under 1122 is a voluntary federal program; Certificate of Need (CON) review was mandated by P.L. 93-641, but is a state program requiring passage of state legislation. Today all states except Idaho have 1122 or CON programs, or both, although most do not meet federal requirements.

The State Health Planning and Development Agency

Another structural element established under Title XV of the law is the State Health Planning and Development Agency (SHPDA). Each state participating in the program is required to designate a single state agency to carry

---

*As of the beginning of November 1980 (1 year after the program became fully active), 27 HSA decisions had been overridden, 18 sustained, and 28 cases were still pending, according to the Bureau of Health Planning, Department of Health and Human Services.

out health planning, coordination, and regulatory functions in the state. Just as the HSA must submit an annual work program detailing its investment of resources for a year, the state agency must submit an administrative program for review and approval by the Department of Health and Human Services (DHHS).

The SHPDA is responsible for conducting the state's health planning activities and for implementing those portions of both the state health plan and the HSAs' plans that relate to the government of the state. The state agency also is required to conduct certain regulatory activities. If the state participates in capital expenditure reviews for the secretary of DHHS under Section 1122 of the Social Security Act, the state agency must be responsible for the reviews. In addition, the state agency is required to administer a certification-of-need program that complies with federal statutory and regulatory requirements. As indicated above, the SHPDA also has a role in the appropriateness review program, preparing and making public findings based on its own review as well as that of the HSA.

Statewide Health Coordinating Council

The third structural element to be created under the Health Planning Act is a Statewide Health Coordinating Council (SHCC). The SHCC is intended to provide a forum where the HSA plan documents are coordinated. Sixty percent of the SHCC's members are appointed by the state's governor from among nominees provided by health systems agencies in a state. The SHCC's chair may be appointed by the governor unless she or he declines the opportunity, in which case the chair is elected by the members of the SHCC. The SHCC is responsible for final preparation of the State Health Plan (SHP) based on a preliminary document prepared by the SHPDA, and is charged with the responsibility for ensuring that needs identified by the state program agencies (such as the state public health authority or the state mental health authority) are addressed in the State Health Plan. As a result of the 1979 amendments, the SHCC no longer has final approval authority concerning the State Health Plan. That authority is vested in the governor, who must approve the document. The SHCC is also responsible for reviewing the budgets and applications of HSAs and for advising the

SHPDA in its responsibilities. The SHCC, unlike the SHPDA, is involved in the proposed uses of federal funds, reviewing entitlement programs and federal grants and contracts that involve health resources in more than one Health Service Area. In addition, the act established a national council for advising the secretary of DHHS. This committee's first report recommended an expanded and strengthened role for the council.

Certificate of Need and 1122 Review--State Level

Title XV of the planning law requires that all states participating in the health planning program develop a certificate-of-need program intended to ensure that only those services, facilities, and equipment that are deter- mined to be needed are developed and made available with- in the state. The certificate-of-need concept, borrowed from the public utility regulation field, has been applied to the health industry by several states since the late 1960s. For health planning, Congress mandated states to develop such programs and authorized substantial financial penalties for those states that did not comply.

Congress assumed that prior review and authorization of capital expenditures would help prevent duplication of services and facilities, which, in turn, is supposed to hold down inflation in the health industry. In addition, certificate of need was seen as an instrument for region- alizing the health system and giving power over resource distribution to community and state health planning activities.

The certificate-of-need program was not the first federal effort to control capital expenditures through prior review and approval. In 1972, the Social Security Act was amended to authorize and provide reimbursement for review of capital investments of facilities receiving funds under the Medicare and Medicaid programs.* This review program (Section 1122 of the Social Security Act) is voluntary, and is dependent on a state's signing a contract with the secretary. Under an 1122 program, an agency of state government (usually the state planning agency) is designated to review capital expenditure

---

*This was also the statute that created the PSROs and required medical review of Medicaid patients in nursing homes.

proposals that meet certain criteria. If a proposal is
not approved, the sanction is to withhold a portion of
the federal reimbursement for facilities and services
established despite state disapproval. Under CON the
sanctions are denial or revocation of operating license,
court injunction, and fines. One of the differences
between 1122 and CON is the appeal process. If an
applicant is dissatisfied, the applicant may appeal to
federal officials at DHHS, whereas under CON the appeal
process remains at the state level.

Although it was assumed that Section 1122 review would
be redundant once a state had developed a certificate-
of-need program, delays in the establishment of CON
programs and differences in coverage have led the
federal government to continue to encourage states to
participate in the 1122 program even after a complying
certificate-of-need program is in place. Certificate
of need has been a source of tension between the federal
and state governments because it forces a state to per-
form a function that it might not otherwise undertake.
Some states initiated lawsuits to overturn the requirements (see Chapter 3), but none has yet been successful.

Facilities Construction Assistance

The 1974 Planning Act also revised federal financial
assistance for health facilities construction. In a
new Title XVI, the Hill-Burton program was replaced by
a more modest effort focused on modernization of
medical facilities, construction of new outpatient or
ambulatory facilities, and conversion of existing medical
facilities to permit the provision of new types of health
services. The 1979 amendments added authority for
federal grants to assist institutions in discontinuing
unneeded services and converting unneeded facilities to
other uses, but no money has yet been appropriated. Money
for construction of new inpatient medical facilities was
authorized only in areas that experienced recent rapid
population growth.

Implementation of Title XVI has been slow. The only
component for which significant appropriations have been
made available is a project grant program for modernization of public medical facilities. Reflecting strong
pressure from urban law makers, $11 million was appropri-
ated in 1976, and another $39.8 million was "reprogrammed"

for grants to public medical facilities. No additional money has been appropriated since then.

While there is little money for facilities, the older Hill-Burton program still serves as the authority and backdrop for actions to improve equity in access to health services and reduce discrimination. Hill-Burton-assisted facilities are required to provide uncompensated ("free") care to residents of the area (worth either 3 percent of operating costs* or 10 percent of Title VI assistance). This obligation extends for 20 years for grants or until the loan is paid back.† Such facilities must serve all residents of their service areas without discrimination. The enforcement of those requirements has been viewed as an opportunity to enhance sensitivity to the poor and minorities and improve access. Hospitals have vociferously objected to the requirements. A study by another committee of the Institute of Medicine for the Office for Civil Rights is examining some of these issues.

Area Health Services Development Fund

Title XVI also provided authority for the establishment of an area health services development fund in each Health Service Area. This fund, managed by the HSA, was to provide small grants and contracts for projects that supported the HSA's plans. The development fund would represent the only flexible implementation funds available directly to and administered by the HSA, as a replacement for the development funding available under the earlier Regional Medical Programs. Enactment of this provision indicated that the Congress was concerned with providing resources to encourage the implementation of the HSPs so that they would not be viewed as a "paper planning process." But funds never have been appropriated to establish or test the area health services development fund concept. Thus, in practice, the incentive potential of planning has never been realized--or even tried. The

---

*Minus Medicaid/Medicare reimbursement.

†Title XVI contains slightly different assurance requirements. Authorized funds carry a permanent community service obligation.

absence of flexibility and of "seed money" to use as a
catalyst in promoting implementation is frustrating and
disappointing to planners and volunteer participants in
the health planning process. A survey by the American
Health Planning Association found this problem was often
cited as limiting flexibility, thus causing frustration.

Program Funding

Funds for the planning program have always been modest.
The total amount of money appropriated for all of the
federally sponsored health planning and regulatory
activities under Title XV was $174.5 million in FY
1980. The HSAs received $124.5 million of that total,
but severe cutbacks in the program were proposed for
FY 1981.

Summary of Overview of the Health Planning Law

The structural and functional provisions of P.L. 93-641
have been viewed by many as a revolutionary departure
from previous practice concerning health planning.
But they were built on lessons from several earlier
activities, including private areawide health planning
agencies, and voluntary hospital councils. It is useful
to remind the reader, as does Katharine Bauer, that:

> Health planning and health regulation as spelled
> out in the law are, in fact, just an overlay of
> new incentives and controls in an extraordinarily
> complicated industry in which an already extensive
> system of informal planning and voluntary, quasi-
> governmental, and governmental controls are being
> continually exercised. A body of law and volun-
> tary agreements reflecting the cumulative de-
> cisions and decision-making rules of many diverse
> organizations now, as always, determine the actual
> operational plans of the nation's 380,000 physi-
> cians, its 7,000 acute care hospitals and its
> many other health services providers. . . .
>   A host of factors, singly and in interaction,
> make the U.S. health care system what it is and act
> to obstruct fundamental changes that rational plan-
> ners might believe to be desirable. (Bauer, 1977)

INTERNAL STRESSES IN THE PLANNING PROGRAM

The restructuring of the planning program has created
tensions in intergovernmental relations and relations
between the public and private sectors in the health care
field. The act's insistence on an expanded consumer role
in the planning process also has created problems as
traditional power relationships in the health industry
are threatened.
  The program is hampered by further problems not yet
discussed here:

  • There is no concept in the planning law of a regional or functional health care budget or of a need to
  match expenditures to revenues.
  • There is no concept in the planning law of an overall limit on capital expenditures to determine the level
  of new health investments. Without such discipline, it
  is likely that the multiple perspectives on boards will
  produce a list of wishes and few incentives to bargain
  for limited resources.
  • There is not even a hypothetical notion of what
  might be purchased within a limit of this year's expenditure. The disparity between the pressures on
  state government and HSAs in this regard exacerbates
  intergovernmental problems (Vladeck, 1980).
  • There is virtually no connection--geographically,
  temporally, economically, even psychologically--between
  the costs of the services or equipment being petitioned
  for and of the funds available for paying for the
  services.
  • There is little recognition of the concept of
  affordability, yet planners are tied, by statute and
  the courts, to a tradition of determining "need."*

-----

*One scholar suggested that planners should abolish the
word "need" from their vocabularies. They should stop
asking how many beds are needed and ask instead: "How
many beds are part of an efficient plan for providing the
level of services this community has decided it can afford
and is willing to pay for?" (Roberts, 1979). But there
is no mechanism by which the community decides what it
can afford (others outside the community are most often
the direct payers) and no way of expressing a willingness
to pay.

• Planning agencies deal with problems that are poorly understood by the public and not well understood by public officials and professionals. Without heightened public awareness, efforts to modify health services, particularly if the public perceives that it will lose some service or facility, will often fail or be overturned. New questions are being raised, for instance, challenging conventional wisdom about advantages and disadvantages of hospital closings.

• Health planning is dependent on how much is known from medical science and health services research concerning efficacy of treatment and the appropriate supply of services.* Without adequate technical information, untested assumptions and opinions affect the decision process. Without a strong knowledge base from the research community, it is possible for planning agencies to become prey to the demands of special interests that are organized and can follow each issue with a concentration of resources and information. Citizen participation may counterbalance such interests, but more research and good data are needed.

• There is an impatience with programs of this sort in this country. It is not clear whether the Congress and the planning program's supporting coalition will recognize the importance of institutional maturity

---

*Alternative approaches to determining appropriate supplies of health services are discussed by Arnold S. Relman in "Determining How Much Medical Care We Need," *New England Journal of Medicine*, Nov. 27, 1980, p. 1292. Relman points out the need for studies of small, well-defined populations. He cites a study by Robert H. Kennedy *et al.* (published in the same issue of the *New England Journal of Medicine*) in which the use of cardiac catheterization by residents of Olmsted County, Minnesota, is analyzed. This study looks at a population that receives all specialized hospital care within the county from salaried physicians whose decisions are assumed not to be influenced by nonmedical considerations. The findings of this study are therefore a good basis for estimating the need for cardiac catheterization. More studies of this kind would be helpful in estimating need for different services.

and long-range capacity building and allow the program
time to achieve anything worthwhile.*
• We must point out, although we cannot estimate, the
seriousness of the negative consequences of executive
branch budget cuts, more federally dominated national
bed reduction schemes, and the threat of antitrust
litigation.

Nor can we gauge the effects of uncertainty and
changes in policies on the ability to recruit, educate, and retain planners. A cadre of technically com-
petent, sensitive, and experienced planners is essential
to the program. Talented people will not long endure
unnecessary stress, lack of opportunities for personal
satisfaction and self-esteem, and relative job in-
stability. It is not by accident that the median age
of many planners, including executives, is low, and
staff turnover is high.

Staff turnover has many negative effects (see both
Brown and Morone in Volume Two), including changes in
technical approaches, making volunteers feel uncertain
about difficult decisions.

Planning in the 1980s will be even more difficult
than in the late 1970s. The most intense struggles in
the 1980s will stem from the need to replace or modernize
existing facilities and services. The decisions concerning new projects and services in a well-endowed health
system are quite different from decisions about replacing
and renovating services in the old system. Planners will
face tougher legal questions, and difficult issues of
licensure, certification, and regulatory authority.

The complexities of the 1980s will make even more
pressing the questions of governance and accountability.
We do not know whether methods for ensuring public
accountability of the health systems agencies are adequate
(but these are discussed in Chapters 3 and 4). It is not
obvious what the long-run relationship should be between
the quasi-public HSAs and other public bodies and how

---

*Full designation of HSAs has been slow, which makes it
particularly important to allow more time for agencies
to mature, rather than evaluating the program as if it
were fully implemented in 1975. By the beginning of 1978
only nine out of 205 HSAs were fully designated (the remainder being conditionally designated). By February 1979
the number of fully designated HSAs had risen to 171. Thus,
for the majority of HSAs, their life as fully designated
bodies only started during 1978.

the relationships might be affected by new developments.

Further, the composition of the governing body reflects a particular model of advisory bodies--the people being regulated and planned for as an integral part of the process. The committee does not feel that the current structure, including the types of agencies and who participates, should be changed at this time. There are solid reasons for learning from what has been done.

PURPOSES AND EXPECTATIONS

At the end of its first year's report, *the committee concluded*:

> *. . . that the current health planning program has substantial potential for helping to achieve certain important social goals, through local planning for improved local health care systems.*

The committee continues to hold that view. In the course of its deliberations, the committee was presented with both anecdotal and empirical evidence of the planning program's successes, as well as its problems. The fact that these successes are often dimmed by perceived problems with the program is not surprising. The committee noted earlier that if the program is not living up to all the expectations of the various interests involved in its design and operation, the problem may be with the expectations, rather than the program itself.

It would be logical to assume that a program with the structural complexity and breadth of responsibility of the health planning program would create divergent expectations at the various levels involved. The committee found this to be the case, as reflected both in the studies performed and the testimony received. The major discontinuity in expectations is between the federal and local levels. In framing the basic legislation, Congress stated 11 national priorities for health planning, and expanded the list to 17 in the 1979 amendments. Despite the wide range of topics encompassed in the priority list, such as medical care organization, professional training, improved management of health enterprises, community health education, and health promotion, the subsequent actions of the Congress and the administration have made it clear that the expectation is for cost containment in the institutional sector. Cost containment has become the goal against which some members of Congress and the executive branch judge the effectiveness of the program, despite the limited abilities provided to planning agencies for controlling expenditures of health providers.

At the local level, cost containment is viewed as a worthwhile goal, but not the only one. Local agencies have, as reflected in their plans and actions, a broader agenda of concerns--particularly improved access to services, health promotion, and disease prevention. Conflicting goals between levels have contributed to perceptions at both levels that the program is not functioning effectively. The federal level sees the program as ineffective in cost containment. The local level perceives that the program is ineffective in responding to local, rather than federal, needs.

The committee concluded that the demonstrated differences between the goals professed in the act and those applied by federal administrators and the Congress in evaluation may lead to invalid conclusions concerning the program's continuation. The committee recommends that a clearer statement of purposes and expectations of the health planning program be developed as a basis for evaluation of its effectiveness. This statement should recognize the limitations imposed by the level of program funding and authority and provide better direction to both levels concerning the program's activities. Goals should be internally consistent, or inconsistencies should be explicitly recognized. Until such goals are developed, health planning will be vulnerable to buffeting by conflicting values and changing priorities.

This does not mean that the program would not have several goals that may sometimes be contradictory. Public policy must often pursue seemingly incompatible goals simultaneously (Vladeck, 1979). Each goal has value, and it is the very fact that the choices are hard, touching highly personal elements in our lives and involving deeply held values that makes a process like planning so important. Clarity about those conflicts and acceptance of the process must be recognized.

Connected to the need for well-defined goals is the need for a reasonable set of expectations for the health planning program. "Reasonable" can be defined in several ways: reasonable in the sense of technical and political feasibility; reasonable in relation to the limited

authority of the agencies; reasonable in terms of the
dollars and staff of the agencies; or reasonable in
terms of the length of time that the agencies have been
functioning. Fixing more clearly the objectives of the
program would permit more rigorous evaluation and
identification of a range of planning methods.

It is difficult, if not impossible, to try to
understand national, state, and local roles and relationships in health planning or consumer participation without some overall notion of what the planning agencies
are trying to achieve. It is hard to talk about effective
intergovernmental relations or an effective consumer if
there is not at least some broad idea of what the program is supposed to accomplish. The absence of agreement on the program's purposes, and of associated, well-
publicized, and sensible performance measures creates
confusion.

Another important reason for trying to identify
realistic goals for the planning program is a tendency
to confuse the aims of health planning with other programs. There is a nationwide PSRO program, a number of
state rate-setting commissions, thousands of health
departments, and many other national, state, and local
health programs all relating to one or more of the goals
subsumed under broad health planning goals. The role and
function of the planning program should be more clearly
outlined in relation to the other initiatives. Planning
must embrace all of these functions to some extent and
reconcile the opposing values in their planning and review functions.

Role clarification is important for evaluative purposes but it has other values as well. The current
planning program includes an experiment with an unusual
structure for advising on investments in health services.
Many aspects of the program are untested, their effects
and their value unknown.* Studies for evaluative purposes will help our understanding of social/political
experiments in the United States. Lessons learned about
shifting the balance of power in medical care, estab-
lishing more effective means for allocating resources in
the health sector, and making the health system more accountable to the public will find increasing application
as federal investment increases in financing of health
services.

---

*Downs' paper, in Volume Two, discusses this at length.

It is important to note that clarifying the objectives of the planning program may have some negative as well as positive effects. For example, some interests in the coalition that today supports health planning may be alienated by some specific program goals. Thus, political support will be weakened. Reconciling internal contradictions in the planning program will be of sufficient benefit to justify the opposition that will follow. But clarifying expectations will also reveal new problem areas and internal ambivalences such as the relationships with the federal health care systems.

It is possible, of course, that the Congress will support the degree of decentralization in the planning structure and the planning/resources allocation and decentralization system as values in their own right. There has been less enthusiasm in the executive branch, especially the Office of Management and Budget, for supporting such a locally directed system. Certainly, it needs to be clear that the particular structure will, at its best, produce an open forum for the community to work out what it wants to see invested in health. It will reflect the community and mirror its virtues and weaknesses, but it also can modify public understanding of health issues and lead to changes in attitudes and desires concerning the support of less costly health care activities. On the other hand, if some perceptible reductions in the rise of expenditures do not occur in areas that health planning agencies can influence (i.e., capital expenditures), it is possible that another mechanism will be set up, and the HSAs role viewed as an expensive appendage.

It is the committee's judgment that the purposes of the planning program for which the program could be, and should be, held accountable, in their order of importance, based on the program's nature and authority, are:

1. *To establish and maintain an open, participatory structure for articulating community health needs and desirable alternatives for meeting those needs, to be used in advising both governmental and private sector decision-makers who control health resources at the local, state, and national levels;*

2. *To contribute to the redirection of the health system, through planning for a more effective, accessible, higher quality and more efficient configuration of facilities and services that is*

*more closely matched to basic health care needs
of the area's population. This should include
developing a carefully thought out position for
dealing with the introduction of new technological
advances into the health care system, with sensitive consideration and fair-minded appraisal of
all important factors, not only costs. Done properly,
this purpose whould lead to a contribution in the
overall containment in the rise of health expenditures,
so this purpose and the next one (3) are not truly
separable. However, specifying a cost containment
mission, as well, within the proper context, is
important to ensure that the committee is not misunderstood.*
*3. To contribute to the "containment of health
care costs," that is, to contribute to moderation
in the rise of health care expenditures, primarily
through planning a more cost-effective health system (as noted in 2), through efforts to improve
the health status of the population, especially
through programs that promote health and prevent
disease, and efforts to limit unnecessary capital
investment and direct such investment toward more
cost-effective facilities and services.*

It is important that this use of "cost containment"
not be confused with budget cuts for health and social
services, particularly for low-income, old, and disabled
citizens. A more cost-effective health system that meets
the requirements of citizens can be achieved through
improvements in the deployment of technology and high-
cost services. Planning is aimed at a better match
between requirements and services, not at cutting out
the services for which reimbursement is currently inadequate. The federal government's preoccupation with
the idea of cost containment has undermined the planning
aspect of the program.

Improving the health of the people is the overriding
goal of the planning system. However, given the sometimes indirect link between changes in health services
and incremental improvements in health status, and the
difficulty of measuring such changes in the short term
and attributing them to the health planning agencies'

actions, it is unreasonable to judge the program on short-
term health status changes.*

A major interest of the committee was to call for a
fair, realistic evaluation of the health planning program in terms of the local systems that it was intended
to affect, not only the nation as a whole. In effect,
while the program is aimed at making an overall difference in the way that health resources are deployed in
this country, any fair evaluation of the program must be
disaggregated. Planning is a national investment, and
a fair question to ask is whether or not this is a good
public investment by the federal government. But the
answer must be reached by looking at the achievements of
many different areas and whether or not the respective
publics are benefitting from this planning. It will
be difficult to combine the findings from individual
systems in any acceptable quantitative manner. For
example, is a failure in Los Angeles balanced by success
in four middle-sized communities, thereby supporting a
conclusion that the program was not a failure overall?
Certainly, given the visibility and size of a city like
Los Angeles, it will take a number of solid program
successes to balance negative perceptions resulting from
a failure. But the fact that this is a nationwide program with nearly 300 agencies, and thousands of volunteers
should inhibit tendencies to generalize about it too
often.

Agreement is needed on the definition of national
interest as it relates to health planning, and on what
level of return for the planning investment is acceptable.
Given the size and diversity of the nation, the evidence
will be mixed. Trends and overall findings will be the
only evidence concerning what is happening.

Several fundamental characteristics of evaluative
studies of social/political "experiments" are relevant
to the consideration of evaluation in health planning.
It takes time for organizations to take root, develop
"name recognition," visibility, and either develop or
fail to develop credibility and an accepted role in the
community (Klarman, 1976, 1978). The amount of time required varies according to a number of factors including
the history of similar activities in the area. For
example, a long history of voluntary health planning in

*This point is discussed by Downs in Volume Two.

Rochester, New York, promoted rapid development of health
systems planning because the community could understand
what the work of the new agency meant. Until the planning program reaches a level of maturity, an evaluation
can only count intermediate steps toward something.
Movement in the right direction, however, should not be
considered trivial. It is critical that the time variable be accepted as important and be fully considered
in research and analysis.

Policymakers and program administrators often express
concern over the importance of personalities in the success, failure, or mediocrity of a program. The health
planning program is not exempt from the reality that it
will take the talent, drive, and commitment of individuals
to enable it to fulfill its promise. But the policy
question is what factors attract or repel the more
talented to participate and how the program might be
structured to draw in more talented, responsible, and
concerned men and women and keep them interested in
struggling with a new social institution in a difficult,
unfriendly environment. It should also be remembered
that the planning system exists today, and some depend on
it. Planning has value and merit to those, such as
third-party payors, who benefit from and are users of
planning policies.

Measures

Once some agreement is reached on the purposes of the
program, it will be easier to isolate possible effects
and measures of effectiveness. For example, the resource
standards issued by DHHS are aimed at a more effective
and efficient system--through reduced duplication of
services and equipment and higher-quality care.* The
standards have received wide distribution and embody
goals that are suited to a planning process intended to
take into account complex trade-offs, so they are good
starting points for overall measures. It should be

---

*Standards issued to date cover acute care beds, computed
tomographic scanners, obstetrical services, neonatal
special care units, pediatric inpatient services, open
heart surgery, cardiac catheterization, radiation therapy,
and end-stage renal disease. These standards were subjects
in the committee's first-year report (Institute of Medicine, 1980).

noted that serious questions continue to be raised concerning some of the assumptions underlying certain of the
established national resource standards. Members of this
committee were uncomfortable about using standards that
may be based on questionable assumptions as measures of
effectiveness of the program. There are barriers to
simple use of the national standards as proper indicators
of the success of the planning agencies. First, standards
may appropriately be modified by special local conditions.
Second, because planning agencies cannot control the
supply of services, progress toward the standards may
be beyond the influence of the agencies. Third, planning
actions are most likely to take time to make a difference,
and be discernible only in reported statistics after a
time lag. Finally, standards may have undesired and un-
predicted side effects. It is the conviction of this
committee that the immediate effects that can be ascribed
directly to planning are whether or not agencies have
specifically addressed problems in their areas, including
those high-lighted in the national guidelines, and
whether they have proposed plausible, affirmative steps
for correcting any problems.

In the balance of this section, the committee restates
what it believes to be reasonable purposes and suggests
some specific methods for evaluating the health planning
program.

RESTATEMENT OF PURPOSES AND DISCUSSION

Purpose I

> To establish and maintain an open, participatory
> structure for articulating community health needs
> and desirable alternatives for meeting those
> needs, to be used in advising both governmental
> and private sector decision-makers who control
> health resources at the local, state, and national
> levels.

The establishment of the health planning forum and the
proper composition of the governing body--at least in
terms of structure and sociodemographic characteristics--
can be measured in reported statistics. Although such
descriptive characteristics are useful in ascertaining
whether or not the program's requirements for ensuring

broad representation are being met, they do not ensure
that the forum is a good or effective one for the community.

To determine how well the system is working, the
questions listed below should be asked of major public
health, consumer, provider, insurance, planning, and
service organizations and other opinion leaders. Any
point of view may reflect antagonisms based on a variety
of factors unrelated to agency effectiveness, so analysis
of the data needs to be handled carefully. However, in
the aggregate, if the perceptions are very bland or
negative, clearly, there are problems. In addition, care
is needed because HSAs and SHPDAs are dealing (or should
be) in some of a community's most sensitive issues, and
health planners can be viewed in unflattering ways. It
is because of the inevitable and, one could hope, con-
structive conflict, that the postures of fair-mindedness,
high-quality data and analyses, and institutional integ-
rity and credibility are so important.

Questions to be asked include:

1. Has the HSA developed credibility in the community?
2. Has the HSA created a useful and fair-minded forum
for public policy discussion on health issues?
3. Has the HSA shown leadership in catalyzing interest in and worked to solve critical issues, including
health problems of minorities, the handicapped, and the
mentally ill?
4. Has the HSA focused additional attention on areas
of unmet need?
5. Is the HSA pressing for innovative approaches to
solving complex problems of access/quality cost trade-
offs?
6. Does the HSA serve as an effective agent in
helping others to improve the quality and relevance of
health care services received by the public?
7. Does the HSA help to promote the health of the
residents of the area directly or by working with other
agencies and institutions that have that as their primary responsibility?
8. Is the HSA involving new groups in considering
health issues?
9. Is the HSA actively working to raise awareness of
promises and pitfalls of less traditional services or
approaches?
10. Has the governing board managed to use consumers
and others for effective advice on public policy?

11. What were the major health care decisions in the community last year and how did the HSA contribute to the decision-making?

In addition, the study should ascertain what the HSA's governing body members think about the organization and how the SHCC and SHPDA perceive the HSA. Finally, the effect of the HSA and the SHPDA on state decision-making could be studied.

Specific facts also can be collected. Reporting systems, for example, can determine (1) if the HSA governing body reflects a good mixture and balance of the principal actors in the health system, and (2) if the HSA receives dollar or in-kind services support from local government or the private sector. Health Systems Plans should be reviewed. The plans developed by the agency demonstrate the level of the understanding of health issues by the extent to which the agency has identified and proposed plausible solutions to critical health problems and by the rationale for selecting certain priority goals and activities. Plans are a source of evidence concerning the quality of the program.

Purpose II

To contribute to the redirection of the health system through planning for a more effective, accessible, higher-quality and efficient configuration of facilities and services, which is more closely matched to basic health care needs of the area's population, including carefully thought out positions for introducing new technology.

Measures of the activities and effectiveness of health planning will reveal evidence of the steps the agencies take to change the configuration of health services toward improved quality, increased accessibility, and other goals.

The national resource standards represent quantitative measures that have received wide publicity and enjoy reasonable acceptance, at least as benchmarks, throughout the nation. They represent targets toward which planning agencies should be moving aggressively and they represent sensible markers for planning.

As discussed earlier, the emphasis in evaluation
should be on identifying how the planning agencies have
worked to redirect the health system and what steps they
have taken to effect change in their own areas. A
methodology to do this was designed and tested by the
Urban Institute (Bell, 1978) and should be studied further. Parts of the approach are being used at the Bureau
of Health Planning.

Purpose III

To contribute to the "containment of health care
costs," that is, to contribute to moderation in
the rise of health care expenditures, primarily
through planning a more cost-effective health
system (as noted in Purpose II), through efforts
to improve the health status of the population,
especially through health promotion and disease
prevention, and through efforts to limit unnecessary
capital investment and direct investment toward
more cost-effective facilities and services.

One of the primary purposes of the health planning
program, as currently structured, is to control the rate
of increase in health care expenditures through modifying
capital investment. Not only is there a desire for an
overall decline in the rate of increase in expenditures,
but there is also an interest in a shift in capital investments to other activities, such as preventive services and
those that promote health (e.g., smoking cessation, hyper-
tension, and weight control clinics).
Two types of evaluative questions need to be answered:

1. Is there a slowing (adjusted for inflation) in the
rise of capital investment and operating expenses that
can be attributed to the planning/regulatory apparatus?
2. Is capital being redirected in the health sector?
Are the capital investments approved by the planning
agency more cost-effective than those denied? The answers
to these questions will vary substantially by region, by
state, and within states. For example, some areas with
very old physical plants have extensive needs for renova-
tion and modernization. Other areas may be medically
underserved or have growing populations requiring new
services or facilities. In the aggregate, a substantial

deceleration of new facilities and services should be
occurring.

It must be emphasized that aggregate statistics are
not very informative and can be misleading. The best
way to find out whether or not capital investment controls
are having an effect of any significance is to analyze the
data on a substate basis and/or a sample of individual
projects. Problems with data, techniques, unit of analysis, stage in investment cycles, and attribution should
inhibit generalization. This is not to say that rigorous
studies should not be done, rather that they should be
done on a substate basis and with sensitivity to the number
of confounding factors.* Studies such as Howell (1980) are
examples of the kind that should be undertaken in other
places as well to begin to understand the dynamics in the
industry.

Studies (including the Institute of Medicine, 1976)
have shown that there are too many hospital beds in the
United States. Planning strategies for most areas should
be aiming at a reduced bed complement through mergers
or closings and provision of lower-cost alternative services. Mergers or closings should be monitored to ensure
that the cost containment pressures do not result in an
increase in underserved populations.

To summarize, the committee believes that it is
important to state what can reasonably be expected and to
assess program performance against that standard. The
health planning program cannot accomplish all that
political rhetoric has demanded of it. The critical
question, however, is what can it reasonably be expected to accomplish? Would those accomplishments, if
achieved, warrant continuation of the program? And
are those goals being achieved? This committee has concluded that the health planning program cannot be expected, by itself, to resolve the various difficulties
that the American health sector faces. It believes, however, that the program can make a contribution toward
such resolution. Even the more limited objectives and
expectations are worth pursuing and the committee offers
specific recommendations to improve program operation.

------

*See Downs and Cohodes in Volume Two for a discussion of
the problems of evaluation studies and some suggestions
for appropriate study techniques.

A recent statement by Klarman (1979) succinctly cap-
tures the spirit of this chapter and the intent of the
committee.

> Much less regulation would be a good thing,
> if it were not in conflict with other fixed fea-
> tures of our health care system such as third-
> party payments, direct reimbursement to providers,
> and consumer ignorance. The foreseeable level of
> regulation in health care is likely to be high.
> Yet it should only be sufficient to accomplish
> its stated purposes. Regulation, as well as plan-
> ning, should be open, conducted with due process,
> and visibly fair. With local participation and
> with focus on the concrete health care problems
> of communities and populations, there may develop
> a substantial willingness to adopt the recommenda-
> tions of HSAs and to abide by the results. That
> is what one would hope for in our type of society,
> with its mixed set of institutions, diverse prefer-
> ences, and pluralistic governance.

3   NATIONAL, STATE, AND LOCAL
ROLES AND RELATIONSHIPS

The results of the committee's study of national, state,
and local relationships in the health planning program
are discussed in this chapter. The first section provides background information for an understanding of the
strengths and limitations of the program. The second
section discusses issues brought to the attention of the
committee at the public hearing and in written testimony.
The last section presents the committee's recommendations
for improving the functioning of the program in respect
both to vertical national, state, and local relationships
and horizontal relationships at each level.

There are few industries in the United States more
fragmented or diversely controlled than the health care
enterprise. The characteristics of the health system at
the operating level result from public and private forces
directed horizontally at local, state, and national levels
as well as vertically among those levels. Public agencies
at each level are engaged in financing, regulating, and
delivering traditional public health services and coexist
with a substantial private voluntary system for delivering
similar services. The majority of personal health care
services are delivered by individual or organizational
providers on a voluntary fee-for-service basis, but a
significant portion of medical care services, particularly for the poor and disadvantaged, are delivered through
public hospitals and clinics financed by general tax
revenues of state and local governments, and through
federal programs.

Government has had an increasing role in the financing
of health care services for specific segments of the
population, yet many of its payments for services are made
through private insurance organizations operating as

fiscal intermediaries. The education of health professionals takes place in public and private universities
and other training institutions. The interests of private
nonprofit hospitals and proprietary hospitals, though
both are in the private sector, are sometimes divergent.
This pluralism in the health care system of the United
States is usually regarded as a strength of the system.
It also creates a variety of interest groups with different stakes in the structure and operation of the system.

Many of these interest groups have aggressively and
successfully resisted centralization in the financing
and organization of health care services. It is not
surprising that a complex health planning structure has
evolved over the past 30 years. The lack of political
enthusiasm for centralizing financing or organization
of health services, or for making the system more "public,"
affects planning as well as the operation of the system.*
But there also is an historical resistance to "planning"
in this country.

While the current structure of health planning is
decentralized, the federal government is clearly the
"senior partner."† The federal statute prescribes the
structure and functions of both local and state level
planning agencies and establishes a complex of administrative regulations, operating policies, and program guidelines promulgated and administered by the Department of
Health and Human Services (DHHS). Congress provided
national priorities in the statute, and authorized the
secretary of DHHS to develop additional national guidelines and resource standards to shape state and local
planning documents and related implementation activities.
The secretary of DHHS has the authority to alter planning area boundaries proposed by a governor; has the

---

*The essentially private nature of the health care delivery
system affected congressional action in 1974. Federal financing of health care, although increasing, still represented less than half of the total expenditures for health
care in the United States.

†P.L. 93-641 required state legislation to implement CON,
acknowledging the importance of state authority. The act
could have strengthened the existing federal capital control lever (Section 1122--of the 1972 amendments to the
Social Security Act, Medicare, and Medicaid) and a more
heavily federal partnership.

final say concerning HSA designation; determines when
HSAs are capable of carrying out their full responsibilities; and determines whether or not agency plans and
procedures are technically acceptable. In developing their
planning documents, the local and state agencies are
required to use cost-constraining/quality-enhancing
resource standards (such as standards for the number of
open heart procedures per unit) promulgated by the
federal government. If they do not, they must justify
their divergence from the federally desired directions.

This litany of federal approvals, checks, and rules
suggests a program in which the federal government exer-
cises almost total control, achieving centralized planning through a superficially decentralized model. But
that is not the manner in which it eventuates. Legislative authority contains important constraints on the
ability of the federal government to control state and
community health planning activities. For example, in
the case of local agency approval or disapproval of uses
of selected federal public health funds (a major plan
implementation activity), the secretary's grounds for
overriding HSA decisions are limited by statute and
regulation. The secretary is required to accept local
and state agency adjustments to the national guidelines
for health planning when the adjustments are supported
by data demonstrating special circumstances within the
area or state. And the federal government has no role in
the review and disposition of individual projects under
CON--the most powerful regulatory instrument in the program. Also, the secretary has limited power to terminate
designation and funding of local and state agencies, and
again, administrative due process mechanisms protect
agencies from arbitrary termination. The functional
components of agency activities--plan development, project
review, decision-making--are either not limited by federal authority or protected from arbitrary federal action
by due process and administrative review requirements.

Consistent with the pluralistic nature of the health
delivery system, the health planning legislation allocates
specific functions to the local and state agencies and
mandates linkages between them in carrying out these
functions. P.L. 93-641 emphasized the development of
private, nonprofit area agencies, following the model of
the predecessor Section 314(b) comprehensive health
planning agencies. It was recognized that a community-
based voluntary model might lend HSAs credibility and
enhance their potential for community acceptance.

The federal government's ambivalence toward states is
demonstrated by the relatively minor role originally
given to governors, the limited attention given to state
capacity building, and the comparatively passive activities
assigned to state and governors' offices. None of the
planning actors was given sanctions or authority, and
there was no consideration of a capital expenditures
moratorium or expenditures limit that planning bodies
could use to directly control the explosive growth of
expenditures.

Although the federal government funds HSAs, they are
neither federal nor state administrative entities. The
federal law carefully limits the degree to which local
agencies render "final" decisions, placing greater emphasis on their responsibility for developing plans for
the community's health system and utilizing those plans
as models to guide resource allocation by decision-makers
outside the HSA. An HSA is expected to assist providers
in the community who voluntarily attempt to implement
planning goals; to make recommendations to the state on
capital investment review decisions and the appropriateness
of institutional and other health services; and to approve
or disapprove uses of federal funds (subject to reversal
by the secretary of DHHS under certain specific conditions). In each of these cases, the final decision-making
authority concerning resource allocation is located outside
the HSA. Lest this be perceived as a weakness for the
local bodies, the federal law also limits the conditions
under which decision-makers can overturn or amend an HSA's
recommendation or decision, and provides for administrative
or judicial appeals when a decision differs from the HSA
recommendation.

Because the health planning structure was designed to
accommodate the pluralistic nature of the health care
system, implementation of health planning has created
challenges to the conventional structure of national,
state, and local relationships. Although the health
planning legislation contains substantial detail concerning vertical interrelationships among the component
agencies, it is less effective in defining and providing
tools for the equally important horizontal relationships
at each of the three levels.* In designing a planning

---

*Vladeck (1979) highlighted specific examples of dys-
functional structural elements of the planning network.

system that could accommodate the realities of the health
system, compromises were required. Many of the implementation problems of the health planning legislation
flow from these compromises, as do related problems in
role definition for partipants in planning.

In framing the health planning program, some proponents
in Congress saw it as an essential step preceding national
health insurance. But many factors worked against the
creation of a more centralized planning model. One was
the existence of voluntary community health planning
agencies. Another was distrust of state and local
government on the part of key individuals involved in
drafting the 1974 legislation (see Raab, and Brown). This
led to a legislative package which emphasized voluntary
nonprofit agencies for community planning and limited
the state government role in the overall program.†

Characteristics of Congress also had an effect on the
planning program, particularly on its scope. Responsibilities for health activities are widely diffused within

---

Health service area boundaries that are consistent with
rational technical approaches to planning may be
politically unrealistic and impractical. For example,
health service market areas often cross state borders.
The work of an interstate HSA is complex because it must
be involved with two SHPDAs, SHCCs, and State Health
Departments and various subcommittees.

Vladeck (1979) warned that:

The planning process, rather than encouraging
efficiencies in resource utilization, may actually
accelerate duplication and overbuilding. Residents
of southern New Jersey, for example, have long
sought tertiary care in Philadelphia, but New
Jersey HSAs will experience considerable political
pressure to foster the development of additional
tertiary facilities on their side of the Delaware
River.

†Detailing what was expected of the executive branch, was
intended to reduce the usual delays in promulgating regulations. Such detail was also included because of distrust of the executive branch.

the congressional committee structure.* The committee
responsible for developing the health planning legislation
lacked jurisdiction in several matters that might ration-
ally have been incorporated in a broad health planning
statute. The substantive committees dealing with health
planning had no jurisdiction over such related matters as
the Veterans Administration's health program, Medicare
and Medicaid financing, quality review under the Professional Standards Review Organization program, Section
1122 capital expenditure review under the Social Security
Act, or antitrust responsibilities related to nonregulatory plan implementation. As a result, linkages between
the health planning agencies and the Veterans Administration or PSROs took the weak form of coordination and
cross-representation. Health planning was not tied to
reimbursement, and the issue of conflict between the
aims of planning and existing antitrust laws was dealt
with *only* in the Congress and then not until 1979. Inclusion of such programs as PSRO was perceived as involving too much delay and possible loss of the entire
planning program. These issues that were not dealt with
legislatively have plagued implementation of the law.
The compromises of 1975 have become the problems of 1980.
They are issues that this committee of the Institute of
Medicine concluded should be dealt with directly at the
first legislative opportunity to eliminate some impediments and inconsistencies in health planning policy.

Health Planning as American Federalism

Much in the health planning program is common to other
federal programs and can be regarded as another version
of American federalism. The federal system was created
by a complicated series of compromises and was more
politically pragmatic than administratively or theoretically tidy. Its main purpose was to protect citizens
from abuses of power by limiting the powers of different
branches of government.

---

*For a good discussion of these issues, see Harold Seid-
man, *Politics, Position and Power*, New York: Oxford
University Press, 1980.

The Constitution's framers visualized two levels
of government, each exercising power over the
nation's affairs at the same time, (but) they
failed to make clear what should be the precise
relationship between them or how either level
might relate to local and private sources of
power (Leach, 1970).

A discussion of this is presented by Sapolsky in Volume
Two. Related topics and some consequences of the phe-
nomenon are described by Brown, also in Volume Two.

For the planning program, as for most federal grant-
in-aid programs, there is no guarantee that state
desires and federal requirements will effortlessly gibe
with each other. Indeed, some of the worst intergovernmental snarls develop as the result of conflict
between them (Leach, 1970).

The health planning act also inherited conflicts because of its timing. The act was passed after an era
of generous grants to the states, promises of rejuvena-
tion of state authority, and devolution of controls from
Washington. In many parts of the nation, the dollars
that state agencies had to spend for planning and resources
development were reduced. When the funds available for
all planning and resources development are added together,
it is evident that total planning appropriations fell
after 1975 (Table 1). The planning program, with its
relatively weak role for states, flowed against the tide
of the promised new federalism, sparking activism in
public officials' interest groups. However, as a result
of this interest, a great deal of learning about planning
took place quickly. The situation can be summarized in
the words of several authors:

. . . the brief history of the law reads like
a catalogue of contemporary confusions in American federalism: local governments are spurned
for the partially new, partially redundant HSA
structures, states and counties fight for influence within the framework of the law (Iglehart,
1973).

Federal guidelines are promulgated with little
clarity about how seriously they will (or ought
to) be taken in the communities (Marmor and
Morone, 1978).

TABLE 1 Funding Levels: Appropriations History of Health Planning and Resources Development and Predecessor Programs (in thousands of dollars; fiscal years)

	1970	1971	1972	1973	1974	1975	1976	1977	1978	1979	1980[a]
Comprehensive Health Planning	20,650	22,803	25,935	34,800	38,327	29,400	28,000				
Hill-Burton	185,123	196,521	308,204	203,578	210,445	b	51,760				
RMP	100,000	116,990	102,854	134,625	81,983	50,000	10,000				
Health Planning	NA	NA	NA	NA	NA	10,000	90,000[c],[d]	130,000	145,000[d]	143,000[c]	145,400
Health Facilities	NA	NA	NA	NA	NA						30,000
TOTAL	306,773	336,314	436,993	373,003	330,834	89,400	180,350	130,000	145,000	143,000	175,400

[a] Administration proposal.

[b] This amount was used for sec. 1625 project grants, except for 1 percent ($517,600) set aside for program evaluation.

[c] $2,000,000 transferred to Health Care Financing Administration for rate regulation program.

[d] Twenty-two percent (or $11,400,000) of the amount shown under the Hill-Burton program was used for sec. 1625 project grants in fiscal year 1976 and the balance (approximately $39,000,000) was reprogrammed in fiscal year 1978 to provide additional funds for projects approved under sec. 1624 of title XVI. In addition, the used evaluation funds (as noted under footnote b) were also made available for this purpose.

SOURCE: Bureau of Health Planning Office of Policy Development, February 8, 1979. As cited in U.S. Congress, Senate, Committee on Labor and Human Resources. Health Planning Amendments of 1979, S. Report 96-96 (96th Congress, 1st Session), 1979.

ISSUES RAISED IN TESTIMONY TO THE COMMITTEE

Federal Management

The health planning statute details the structure and
functions of the planning agencies. These details have
been substantially expanded through regulations, policy
documents, and guidelines prepared by the federal administrative agency. The committee heard considerable
testimony in the public hearings suggesting "overmanagement" of the program by the federal administrative agency
and an emphasis on achieving program compliance rather
than providing assistance to enhance program effectiveness.
This testimony echoed problems identified earlier by observers of the health planning program. Some of the complaints are common to other federal programs and grow from
inevitable conflicts and tensions in a federal system.
The most frequently reported complaints about federal
management, in addition to those already discussed in this
chapter, include the following:

   • Local and state observers believe there is federal
insensitivity to traditional local and state roles and
relationships, and little appreciation of the time required to nurture relationships, to develop regulations
and guidelines, and to educate the citizens involved.
   • According to state officials, some federal actions
preempt or override state government, implying that
greater knowledge resides at the federal level. Examples
include the 1979 amendment that will prohibit state
certificate-of-need laws from covering Health Maintenance
Organizations (HMOs), and bypasses state government in the
proposed use-of-federal-funds review, giving only HSAs the
review authority.
   • State officials alleged federal indifference to
state legislative time tables. For example, some state
legislatures are in session or take up new authorizing
legislation only every 2 years. For them, it can be
impossible to meet federal deadlines.
   • State officials lamented that states were asked in
1980 to revise their CON laws on the basis of proposed--
not final--federal rules. At the time, state officials
believed that the states would be expected to revise the
statutes again when the rules were final. "Changing
CON in some states means open warfare and, in many
states, every time they are forced to reconsider CON
their statutes are weakened not strengthened" (Merritt,

1980). The coalition used to pass the statutes often is
not composed of natural allies, nor are there strong
constituencies; assembling support for statutory change
can be difficult and politically expensive.
  • Some state and local officials felt that internal
inconsistencies in federal policies and inadequate
federal funding are evidence of a lack of commitment to
health planning.
  • State budget officials feared that, once federal
support dwindled, federal officials would turn to the
states for continued support, although the states had had
nothing to say about the program's development.
  • Frustration was expressed about a program whose
structure and administration do not seem to take into
account the diversity of health care requirements in
the nation. Some witnesses said that a strong general
direction from the federal government is not balanced
by the flexibility needed to adapt general direction to
diverse circumstances. For example, one official noted
that the program often issues a new national policy to
correct a problem at one or two agencies, which creates
problems for other agencies.
  • A problem in the program's administration, according
to some early observers, was the use of regional offices
to directly oversee the act's implementation. Although
regional-level administration often brings decisions
closer to the people and permits some flexibility, it
also allows unevenness in quality of the program, and
sometimes inequities. Frustration with regional operations and cutbacks in staff positions encouraged a re-
centralization of final authority into Washington. The
solution lies in properly balancing federal and local
direction. Strong general direction from Washington
should allow regional offices to give strong direction
within bounds dictated by Washington.
  Changes in location of authority also left state
and local officials confused about who is in charge.
Local and state officials wondered why they had to consult with regional officials if all decisions are made
in Washington.

Issues Identified by a National Council Subcommittee

This committee is also aware of some specific problems
identified by the Subcommittee on Implementation and

Administration of the National Council on Health Planning and Development:

• Guidelines, directives, deadlines, and other federal demands are often viewed as inconsistent and unrealistic, resulting in distorted priorities and unnecessary consumption of time of agency staff.
• Federal officials at the regional-office level are accused of conducting process-oriented checklist reviews of plans because they are not familiar with local priorities and needs and cannot properly or fairly judge the stature of the agency or the quality of the plans.
• State agency reversal of local recommendations on capital project review sometimes is perceived by the HSAs to be caused by political pressure.
• State agency representatives feel that they did not receive sufficient direction and resources, particularly when the program was being put in place, because the federal government was concentrating on building the HSA network. Even state planners find themselves spending time supporting HSA staff development.
• The activism and role of the Statewide Health Coordinating Councils (SHCC) vary among the states. Some councils actively participate in plan development and review state and local planning agency performance. Others merely act as rubber stamps. Budgetary constraints do not permit the councils to have their own staffs, therefore the more active councils become dependent on the State Health Planning and Development Agency staffs. Yet, SHPDAs in states with passive SHCCs find it difficult to force their councils to act on issues, particularly on controversial ones. It is clear that the SHCCs can help strengthen the planning process by providing an arena for bringing together and resolving differences between the state and local perspectives. When it works well, the SHCCs can also help to provide understanding, legitimacy, and credibility for decisions.

Issues Raised by Recent Federal Policy Directions

Some public officials charge that the 1980 and 1981 budget cuts are examples of the federal government's penchant for starting programs and then, by design or changes in policies or priorities, reducing their commitment.

Planning is a staff function, not a service program,
and thus more liable to budget cuts.

Planning--like research, statistics, and evaluation--
often seems expendable in the short run because many
nonplanners do not see its advantages. The benefits of
planning's regulatory aspect are most manifest to those
concerned with federal and state budgets and third-party
payors. Ironically, it may be the regulatory side that
will keep planning alive, although its supporters feel
that its greatest strength and its probable contribution
to cost containment will be through planning, not regulation. Such planning would be aimed at redirecting resources in the health system toward more health-promoting
services, with a reduced emphasis on costly high technology
and necessary use of sophisticated medical care. The
federal budgetary commitment, as contrasted with general
statements of support, reflects an underlying doubt
about the need for planning and the potential effectiveness of regulation. National policymakers may not be
willing to put sufficient resources into planning to have
a chance of testing its value as a service to the community, the state, and the federal budget.

This committee also uncovered a number of issues that
have gained visibility in recent months as federal
financial support for planning becomes more tentative.*
For example, a standardized approach to health planning
raises a series of specific questions:

• Must planning agencies cover the entire nation?
Could planning programs be concentrated in the areas of the
greatest problems of access, health status, or costs?
If so, who or what should they cover?
• Would it be better to have fewer agencies funded
at an adequate level than national coverage funded at
minimal level?

---

*Agency funding is based on size of the population. This
offers surface equity but it is inequitable since planning
costs vary with geography and distance. Also, large
remote areas are further handicapped by difficulties of
attracting and holding staff. Although some of these
problems have been ameliorated by the small fund for
special needs authorized in 1979, this is not adequate
because the agencies are not even funded to their
authorized level.

• Should health insurers be encouraged to be major financial supporters of health planning? Should Medicare/Medicaid pay a share?

Issues of Certificate-of-Need Effectiveness

The effectiveness of certificate-of-need programs is questioned in any discussions of problems in national, state, and local relations. Recent studies lead to the following generalizations about Certificate of Need (CON). There are enormous interstate and intrastate variations in the program.* The older programs and those with a stronger "will" and "mandate" (see Cohodes) to regulate the system more aggressively have had some effect, notwithstanding, as Bauer observed in a 1978 analysis, that the law was given:

no power to influence where physicians practice, their referral networks, their staff privileges or their degree of cost consciousness when ordering ancillary services;

no power to prevent non-institution-based physicians or others from acquiring facilities and equipment that, for institutions, would be subject to certificate-of-need regulations;†

------

*Apart from such inter- and intrastate differences, a recent study by the American Health Planning Association, "Analysis of Health Planning Agency Activity under CON and 1122," HEW Contract Number 100-79-0121, noted that some differences, such as types of applications received or approved and volume of expenditures required and approved, appear to be associated in some cases with such local characteristics as the size of HSA population, the extent to which HSA areas are rural, and the hospital bed-to-population ratio of the HSA area.

†A recent report in the *New York Times* (11/20/80) describes the purchase of CAT scanners by physicians and notes that about 54 scanners are in place in New York State and about 37 are in private use by radiologists. A scanner manufacturer is reported as saying that 70 percent of machines now on order are for radiologists in private practice. It is clear that the exclusion of physicians from CON is a significant gap in the coverage of health care capital investments.

no power to influence the many federal, state, and local regulatory bodies and voluntary agencies whose decisions may push up institutional costs;

no authority to bring federal hospitals under the aegis of local and state planning and regulation.

The effect of CON is certainly not as significant as proponents of "cost containment and bed closure" would like to see, nor is it as weak or as questionable as critics aver. For example, after a thorough review of CON in Massachusetts, Howell concluded: "The presence of Certificate of Need regulation in Massachusetts, then, has improved institutional capital planning and encouraged the development of cooperative relationships among hospitals. . . . (But) even the presence of a mature program . . . does not force an institution to choose among projects."

The most serious continuing problem of CON is that it has no way to determine or estimate the "need" with some sense of what can be afforded (Bauer, 1977; Cain and Darling, 1979; Howell, 1980; Needleman and Lewin, 1979; Sapolsky, Volume Two). The absence of technical certainty, limitations in knowledge concerning efficacy of treatment and the appropriate supply of services, planning technology limitations, and inadequate data make CON decisions complicated and ultimately the product of value judgments by the decision-makers. It has also been observed that political bargaining is a major factor in CON decisions.

Most comprehensive studies of CON cite and document the changes that occur as a program matures. These include a shift from critical review of number and types of beds to extensive analyses of the development and application of more detailed and more technically defensible standards and criteria for decisions.

A recent report on planning and regulation in New England (Codman, 1979) made the following observations. Contrary to early predictions, the planning system has not been captured by health care providers. Provider interests are often divided. Where providers do not have a direct interest in a project they generally stand on the sidelines, unwilling to use up their own political reserves. Nevertheless, providers can outmaneuver the HSAs and state agencies through multiple strategies, and mobilize a constituency, usually the consumers in their area.

This committee found that even the best evidence
available does not answer the question of relative costs
and benefits of CON programs. It is difficult enough to
measure the costs of the programs;* the benefits are
even less clear. It has been argued that a significant
contribution of the planning program is the acceleration
of sound institutional planning, for which there is a great
deal of anecdotal evidence. However, calculating the
costs and the benefits of such improvements would be hard.
To the extent that the planning program has encouraged
improved institutional planning, circularly, good institutional planning can lighten the task of area planners.
Research should be initiated to discover and disseminate
information on good institutional planning models and on
successful linkages between institutional and area planning.

Because the planning program is more than regulation,
and because the impact of CON and 1122 programs is more
complete than mere disapproval of capital expenditures,
the committee concluded that an assessment of the planning
program on the narrow criteria of approvals and disap-
provals under CON or 1122 project reviews is inappropriate
and likely to be unsatisfactory. The bases on which the
program should be judged are discussed in Chapter 2.

SPECIFIC ISSUES ADDRESSED BY THE COMMITTEE

Relationships with Federal Medical Care Systems

The medical care systems owned and operated by the federal
government, including the Veterans Administration, are
significant elements in the total health care resources
available to the nation. Federal beneficiaries represent
a substantial subset of the population in most health
service areas, and one that often utilizes both the community system and the federal systems. Federal beneficiaries and their resources should be considered as part of

------

*Even the cost of processing applications is hard to
quantify. Cohodes' paper in Volume 2 estimates the cost
to selected state CON agencies of processing an application to vary from $400 to over $7,000.

the community health planning process.* Conversely,
planners for federal systems will undoubtedly want to
take into account an area's total resources when planning
for their eligible populations. In the past few years
a number of steps have been taken to help coordinate health
planning among the different systems. Improvements include having the nonfederal health planners at state and
local levels review and comment on proposals for changes
in federal health services. Participants on all sides of
these complex issues need to develop improvements in
planned linkages, better coordination, and, where appropriate, sharing and regionalization of services.

This committee is aware that two previous committees--
one of the Institute of Medicine and the other of the
National Research Council--have made recommendations on
this subject. However, this committee did not have the
time to explore this problem in depth and does not have
a specific recommendation, except to encourage movement
toward more dialogue in these matters and actions that
will create the most cost-effective health system for all
citizens, including those to whom the federal government
has obligations.

*Recommendations to Expand Coverage of the Planning
Program*

The committee and the authors and speakers at its public
hearing found the relative lack of linkages between planning and financing to be a major barrier to achieving the
goals of the health planning legislation. *In the committee's view, strengthening linkages between health
planning and the reimbursement system should be a high
priority for study in a series of experimental programs
within selected states.* Such linkage might take the
form of a tie between reimbursement under federal programs, and findings that services reimbursed are

---

*Here, as in the first year's report of this committee,
the distinctions between planning and decision-making, and
between planning and regulation, are deliberate. The
committee is not trying to make any statement about the
Congress' decision-making authority in terms of the VA
health care system.

appropriately organized and accord with the plans, criteria, and standards developed and applied by the health planning agencies. *The committee recommends that expanded efforts to link planning and state rate review programs be fostered by the federal government so that the most effective linkage models can be identified.*

While a decentralized planning approach, such as this one, is unlikely, as discussed earlier, to constrain cost increases, other state and federal actions could more favorably influence planning agencies' functions. For example, reimbursement schedules for physicians and hospitals that today favor expensive technology and procedures might be modified centrally to change the incentives. Also, studies funded centrally through the National Institutes of Health, the National Center for Health Care Technology, and other research institutes might help determine what technologies, procedures, and services are medically beneficial and cost-beneficial. With such information, the HSAs might be better prepared to set priorities in the areas they serve.

Another issue is the possible conflict between health planning and antitrust legislation. Congress explicitly required health planning agencies to implement their plans through a variety of means, including securing voluntary cooperation of institutions in regionalization of health services and reductions in redundant services. Although the legislative history suggests that the congressional committee was aware of the antitrust implications of such actions, the legislation itself contained no explicit exemption from antitrust legislation for planning activities undertaken by providers. The issue has since been raised in the courts and with the Department of Justice. Federal court decisions thus far suggest that an implied exemption exists. The Department of Justice, however, has proved unwilling to commit itself on the implied exemption issue, leaving the threat of antitrust action hanging over a variety of implementation efforts.

The committee recognizes that antitrust exemption is only reluctantly granted by the Congress. In this case, however, the public interest in rationalizing the health system and controlling costs must receive priority. The current economics of the American health system preclude effective competition, although major changes in the financing and reimbursement, if made, may affect those conditions. Until that time, the open public nature of the health planning process in itself supplies safeguards against anticompetitive abuse. *Accordingly, the committee endorses the concept of an explicit antitrust exemption for activities publicly undertaken by providers in conjunction with health systems agencies (HSAs), and in accord with the goals, objectives, and recommended actions embodied in adopted health systems plans (HSPs).* The committee recognizes that the issues involved in granting such an exemption are complex and that the exemption language must be carefully structured to prevent abuse. In order to define the issues more carefully, and to develop the most useful legislative language, the committee recommends that the National Council on Health Planning and Development working with the Department of Justice and the Federal Trade Commission establish a task force to develop proposed legislative language. As long as the threat of antitrust action casts a shadow over efforts to secure change through cooperative actions, the pressure will mount to apply regulatory solutions where nonregulatory action would work equally as well. The committee hopes that the council will move expeditiously to begin this important task.

Recommendations Concerning Agency Diversity

The committee's consultants and persons appearing at the public hearing emphasized a need for federal administrators to exhibit more flexibility in the conduct of the health planning program. Some of the planners in the field perceive the program to be "overmanaged" by the federal government. The planning statute is unusually detailed, yet it has spawned extensive supplemental and interpretive regulations, program policies, and program guidelines. The development of such material has been slow, delaying implementation. At the same time, once these policies and regulations are published, agencies are given short deadlines to comply. There are misunderstandings on both sides. Federal administrators, Congress, and others fail to understand the community dynamics that affect changes in board structure, development of consensus plans, or conduct of review procedures. There is a similar lack of appreciation at the community level for the federal regulations process, with its various mandated reviews, sign-offs, and approvals. Considering the detailed nature of the statute, *the committee believes that administrative attention might better be directed to*

*fostering diversity in approaches used by the agencies
(within the broad constraints of the legislation) and
to studying the results, than to efforts to achieve a
high degree of uniformity through inflexibly applied
supplemental regulations.* The operation of this program
could provide an opportunity to learn what works well
or poorly under different conditions. *The committee
recommends that the federal administrators of the program
adopt a policy promoting or allowing natural experiments
in both agency structure and in methods for carrying out
agency responsibilities, and study the results.* Some
opportunity for such experiments already exists within
the constraints of the statute. The committee feels
that even more flexibility is needed. Trial of some
alternative approaches to agency organization and operation will not be possible without changes in legislation.
The committee believes that to enable such experiments to
be performed, Congress, in reauthorizing the planning
program, should make explicit its interest in allowing
experimental approaches to test different ways of health
services planning. The current "controlling" approach
being pursued by the federal administration denies the
federal government, state government, and localities
the opportunity to learn while doing, an essential in-
gredient to any program, but especially one aimed at
creating local institutions with complex missions.

The choices of experiments should be made by the planning agencies, according to size of grant, composition
of staff, and priorities and interests of the governing
body and the state. Accountability should be tied to
the outcome and process goals discussed in Chapter 2.

These recommendations will require more flexibility
than program administrators have permitted in the past.
The emphasis on the part of the administrators of the
program should be on facilitating variations responsive
to a particular community's needs rather than promoting
compliance with excessively detailed administrative
guidance.

The federal government should be firm and clear in
its goals and expectations, and flexible in the means to
achieve those goals that it will allow. There should be
flexibility in the number and nature of agency functions
and responsibilities. Agencies should be permitted to
experiment with more or less frequent plan revisions,
variable cutoffs for certificate of need, methods for
doing appropriateness review, proposed use of federal
fund (PUFF) review requirements, etc.

The committee has already expressed its preference
for the program's having fiscal and temporal stability
overall, with a reasonable level of funding suited to
the required tasks, but *the committee also recommends
that some agencies be better funded to test and document
possible effects of planning with greater funding. In
some cases, the required supplemental money might come
from third-party payors. In addition, some agencies
should be allowed extra Area Health Services Development
Funds for seed money to help get projects started*, as
discussed in Chapter 2.

The range of experiments should be sufficiently broad
to assure the finding of effective new solutions. For
example, some areas could be encouraged to test the
placing of planning units in rate-setting agencies, or of
programs to buy out, convert, and eliminate unneeded
services. Other areas with low health care costs and
little excess capacity might be excellent locations for
raising the capital expenditure review threshold.

It is particularly important to avoid "charting of
outcomes" of experiments. A better understanding must
be developed of the incentives and effects of different
arrangements. The paper by Downs in Volume Two has a
good discussion of these issues. Failure to improve the
knowledge base and technology of planning will ensure
that policy debates continue to be dominated by theoretical
speculations about institutional behavior and untested
assumptions.

Congress must make explicit its interest (through
funding and a legislative history specifying kinds of
experiments) in genuine experimentation in how to effect
change to find the best ways to conduct planning. Contrary to the usual uniform federal approach to problems,
a major goal of this program would be to encourage variation and diversity and to learn more about optimal
methods for allocating resources.

While absence of uniformity and rigid administrative
rules and procedures tends to create anxieties, particularly among Washington policymakers, it is essential that
these fears be overcome by recognition that a program
responsive to national diversity can be more effective
than a uniform program.

Experimentation in Reimbursement and Capital Controls

Reimbursement programs that simply accept or pass through land, plant, and equipment costs as reasonable and necessary encourage investment.

The committee finds that creative reimbursement approaches and new methods limiting nonessential or excessive capital investment are long overdue. The Congress should enact enabling legislation and authorize funds to monitor and evaluate such experiments. There are a wide range of approaches that could be considered, such as:

- a state setting an aggregate limit on capital expenditures for a 3-5-year period;
- state rate regulators imposing per-case reimbursement limits, or studying the experience with this reimbursement in New Jersey;
- federal reimbursement experiments that limit paying for interest, depreciation, rent, and other land costs; and
- federal or state efforts to limit the supply of private loan financing to hospitals or nursing homes.

These approaches would act as impediments to growth of the health industry and force planning agencies to become more selective in making determinations of need. If a special reimbursement program adequately contained expansion, experiments could be conducted in temporarily suspending CON for some elements of the health system.

Recommendations for Stability and Funding

Health planning agency efforts are directed largely to making changes in the health care services and facilities of communities. The components of that structure are often well-established and well-funded. There will be resistance against outside efforts to redirect activities. The health care system has demonstrated great endurance, and health planning agencies are at a disadvantage in working from a base of 3-year authorizations. By placing the planning system at risk every 3 years (and even more often in recent legislative sessions), the Congress erodes the potential effectiveness of the agencies. In the committee's view, longer authorization periods would

help planning maintain the commitment and interest of
its thousands of citizen volunteers and combat resistance
to change in the communities.

Other adverse consequences of the current planning
approach include problems in recruiting and retaining
staff and excessive investment of scarce agency resources
in restructuring programs to respond to triennial adjustments in the basic legislation. Further, although the
program was authorized in 1974 at 50 cents per capita, it
has never had such funds appropriated, and the purchasing
power of that original figure has been eroded by 6 years
of inflation before the program has even been adequately
tested. Accordingly, *the committee recommends that
Congress take the steps necessary to provide a greater
degree of temporal and fiscal stability to the program.*
Among the considerations that should enter into development
of improved legislation are the length of program authorization, the possibility of developing a stable financial
base through use of a trust fund approach for at least
a portion of the funding, and the use of guaranteed
future funding to enable agencies to budget more effectively.

The committee explored the potential for alternative
funding sources for health planning, particularly for
HSAs. Proposals in 1980 from the Office of Management
and Budget concerning HSA funding by third-party payors,
health provider organizations, and state governments, were
given particular attention. *The committee concluded that
funding at the local level by interested parties raised
potential conflicts of interest, or the appearance of
such conflicts. The possibility of influence was also a
factor which makes unwise agency use of money from providers or third-party payors particularly if provided on
a voluntary, rather than mandatory basis.* This problem
was seen as potentially most serious if individual agencies were expected to approach such sources directly
for support. In addition to the potential for conflicts
in planning and project review, there was concern for
the amount of time agencies would have to invest in fund-
raising activities. Although state funding has been provided in some instances, variable state commitment to the
program, as well as the problem of resource availability
at the state level, make that funding undependable on a
nationwide scale. Thus, although the committee under-
stands the desirability of broadening the basis of financial support, it is not optimistic about the feasibility

of such efforts. For the federal government to act on the erroneous assumption that agency funding would be forthcoming from states or other sources would be harmful. *The committee could not reach agreement on how funding for the planning agencies might be broadened without putting other important goals, such as planning agency independence, at risk.* But, *the committee felt strongly that any actions by the federal government based on an assumption that state and local governments or others would pick up funding would be illusory at best.*

The committee recommends that the National Council on Health Planning and Development undertake a special study of the planning agency funding issue, with the goal of producing recommendations for consideration by the Congress during the 1982 review of the authorizing legislation. Particular attention should be paid to securing support from third-party payors and health organizations in a manner that would insulate the HSAs from potential conflict of interest and that would relieve individual agencies from responsibility for direct fund-raising.

Recommendations About Relationships Among Agencies

A particular set of relationship problems for states with a single HSA were reported. In such states, where the population and resource base is not sufficient to support multiple HSAs, concerns were expressed concerning potential and actual duplication of efforts between the HSA and the SHPDA. The committee decided that special attention should be given to dividing functions and responsibilities so as to eliminate duplication or waste. It was concerned that eliminating agencies or turning them into "1536 entities" (that is, agencies in which both state and local functions are carried out) might create problems of access to the agency, especially by consumers, and reduce opportunities for citizen involvement. Because citizen participation is one of the strengths of the planning program, it would be undesirable to constrict it in the name of system efficiency.

At the local level, the health planning structure has an array of horizontal relationships with both governmental and nongovernmental organizations. In a cooperative planning model of this type, such relationships are essential both to the planning process and to implementation of the plans. The range of organizations whose involvement would facilitate the planning process is broad. In some cases (local government, hospitals, HMOs), participation through the governance structure of the planning agency is specified by the statute. In others (PSROs, rate review bodies, regional planning bodies), there is a statutory mandate for the planning agency to exchange information and otherwise involve them in its activities.*

Among the most important of these relationships from the perspective of the committee are those with local official health agencies, which are not directly required to deal with the planning agencies. An expanding interest in disease prevention and health promotion should help to enlist health planning agencies in such activities. Local and state health departments have the major operating responsibility and statutory authority in these areas and are a repository of expertise that should be engaged in planning for such efforts.

The committee concludes that closer operating relationships between health planning and official health agencies should be promoted. This does not require that health planning be conducted by governmental organizations, but rather that such organizations be involved in planning. Michigan is an example of the initiation of systematic efforts to bring planning agencies closer to the health departments in the states.

Other important relationships are those among planning agencies and other federally supported regional bodies. Such bodies, particularly PSROs, collect data and conduct activities for improving the quality of care, also a concern of health planning. The committee recognizes the

------

*Katharine Bauer, in "The Arranged Marriage of Health Planning and Regulation for Cost Containment Under P.L. 93-641--Some Issues to be Faced," *Harvard University Center for Community Health and Medical Care Report,* Series R58-1, December 1977, discusses some special skills and information residing in rate-setting programs that can be of use to HSAs. In particular, rate-setters are conversant with the cost impact of new technologies; have historical data on the cost of introducing certain medical programs and new facilities and their effect on operating costs; and statewide cost/budget data by hospital service area, which can reveal gaps or duplications of services or low occupancy that may indicate a need for sharing services.

differences between the missions of the PSROs and the planning bodies and the real problems that exist concerning data confidentiality. In fact, the committee felt that there is too much attention paid to their working together when their tasks are quite different and the real opportunities for working together are limited. *The committee recommends that the National Professional Standards Review Council and the National Council on Health Planning and Development jointly develop a position concerning data and other information exchange that meets the legitimate need for such data for health planning purposes while observing legitimate concerns regarding confidentiality of individual patient data.*

In this chapter the issues of state, local, and national relationships and relationships among agencies at the three levels were discussed. The committee, recognizing the importance and complexity of such relationships, made such recommendations as to urge flexibility in federal administration of the planning program, experiments in methods of capital control and reimbursement, and expansion of the health planning program to include elements of the health system currently outside the planning framework.

4 CONSUMER PARTICIPATION

This chapter reports the results of the committee's study
of consumer participation in health planning. First,
the history of the consumer participation requirements is
given, with data on its current status. Problems identified in testimony and from the committee's research are
listed. Finally, the committee's conclusions and recommendations are summarized.

HISTORY AND BACKGROUND

An important characteristic of the health planning program is consumer participation. Health Systems Agencies
(HSAs) must have a governing board with a consumer majority and specified numbers and types of health care providers and public officials. Subcommittees and subarea
councils also must have a consumer majority.*
   It is assumed that the inclusion of consumer values
and preferences in the planning process provides a client
perspective on decisions that affect their lives. Consumer needs and preferences are not always different from
those of providers and planners, although each sometimes
resists sharing decision-making power. All interests
should be fully and fairly represented in deliberations
and adequate attention should be given to social and

---

*As a group, consumers on the boards are to reflect the
demographic structure of the health service area (by income, sex, age, ethnic, racial, and linguistic groups) and
represent the handicapped, major purchasers of care (including labor unions), and areas of different population
density.

technical issues. This requires a well-balanced governing body with strong and confident members representing different views.

The 1974 planning law defines "consumers" as citizens who are not providers of health services or do not have a policymaking or fiduciary role in a health institution. Spouses, children, and parents of providers cannot be counted as "consumers." Neither can anyone whose income from occupations related to the provision of health care (such as drug manufacturer, hospital supplies, or research) exceeds one-fifth of total income. Thus most people who have knowledge of the health industry are excluded from participating in planning as consumer representatives. Some feel that has weakened the planning agencies. This is discussed in detail in Volume Two.

The committee examined data from all 204 HSAs and found that consumers make up 52.5 percent of present governing body members (see Table 2). The average size of a governing body is 44, ranging from 15 to 137, and the average size of executive committees is 20, ranging from 6 to 30. Large governing bodies pose difficulties in reaching decisions, governing the agency, and providing adequate staff support. However, a large board provides an HSA the flexibility to accommodate pressures for expanded representation. Sixty-one percent of the agencies use subarea advisory councils to further localize planning and expand opportunities for increased public involvement.

Many agencies reported extensive efforts (beyond compliance requirements) to inform and involve the general public in the health planning process, presumably illustrating a genuine commitment to this activity as well as a desire to develop good will and credibility. Eighty-four percent of HSAs prepare and distribute newsletters reporting agency activities and current health issues; 50 percent maintain an extensive mailing list for distribution of newsletters and other agency documents. Sixty-seven percent have established a speakers' bureau or scheduled presentations, and 74 percent reported cultivation of media relationships as an on-going activity to enhance media cooperation and coverage of agency activities.

The health planning program was designed to help in educating the public about selective health matters and serves to introduce some relatively new participants as advisors to health services decision-makers. One of the important achievements of the planning network has

TABLE 2   Consumers on the Governing Bodies of 204 Health Systems Agencies

	Number		U.S. Population[a]
Total number of governing body members	8,969		
Number of consumers	4,705	(52.5%)	
Number of vacancies	137	(1.5%)	
Total potential consumer positions	4,842	(54.0%)	
Selected characteristics			
Sex			
Females	2,041	(43%)	(52%)
Males	2,664	(57%)	(48%)
Age			
18-34	797	(17%)	(29%)
65+	729	(15%)	(11%)
Income			
Less than $10,000	693	(15%)	(24%)
$10,000-$24,999	2,137	(45%)	(48%)
$25,000 and over	1,605	(34%)	(29%)
Data not provided	59	(1%)	
Income categories changed	211	(5%)	
Race			
Black	695	(15%)	(12%)
White	3,743	(80%)	(86%)
Other--includes Hispanics	267	(5%)	(2%)
Language			
English	4,539	(96%)	(96%)
Spanish	133	(3%)	(2%)
Other	33	(1%)	(2%)

[a] U.S. population figures on sex, age, and race are from U.S. Department of Commerce, Bureau of the Census, *Current Population Reports,* Series P-25, No. 870, January 1980.

[b] U.S. figures on income are from U.S. Department of Commerce, Bureau of the Census, *Current Population Reports,* Series P-60, No. 123, June 1980.

[c] U.S. figures on language are from U.S. Department of Commerce, Bureau of the Census, *Current Population Reports,* Series P-23, No. 60, July 1976.

SOURCE: Data were collected from 1980 Health Systems Agencies' applications for funding and designation.

been the formal, structured addition of consumers to the
world of health policy.

To require that agency governing boards be controlled
by consumer groups was controversial in 1974. Although
more widely accepted now, the notion that other than
health professionals should have a major voice in decisions
about the supply of health resources is still questioned.

The consumer participation requirements are experimental, partly because comparatively little is known about
effective citizen involvement in planning bodies, and
partly because even less is known about ensuring strong
participation by the poor, minorities, and other groups
needing special help to ensure that their perspectives
affect decision-making.

No organized consumer groups were putting pressure
on Congress in 1974 (Caper, 1980), but consumer activist
organizations quickly developed as the health planning
law was implemented. Public interest organizations became
involved as they saw opportunities for strengthening
consumerism in health through health planning (see
Checkoway, Volume Two).

The 1974 law was very detailed, but the consumer
portion said little about board selection processes.
One official said this was because Congress assumed
that agencies could not function or be designated without
broad-based community support, so agencies would work to
ensure that support (Rubel, 1980). The value of broad
support is explained in the House Report on the 1974
legislation.

> Without credibility in the community and close
> working relationships with those who operate the
> health system, guided change will be impossible.
> The credibility and ability to seek change through
> influence and the seeking of assistance can be ob-
> tained in part through the representation on the
> governing body of the HSA of the community's
> change agents and power structure. Thus, while
> a governing body should accurately represent the
> community's consumers of health care, including the
> poor, the rural, and minorities so that their
> needs will be reflected in the agency's plans, the
> governing body should also include representation
> of newspaper editors, judges, bankers, third party
> payers, industry, health professional schools and
> others who, once the plans are drawn up, can

assist the agency in implementing them (U.S. Congress, 1974).

It was hoped that the consumers' numerical superiority would balance the more concentrated interests, and greater resources, information and skills of the providers. It was hoped that inclusion of those prone to criticize the program, especially practicing physicians, would ensure that they would not create problems.

Rationale for Consumer Participation

The 1974 law was written in a way that mixes issues of accountability, participation, and representation.* An underlying assumption was that consumers can, and should, voice the opinions of "the average citizen" and special consumer concerns. The consumer board member group is to "mirror" the community in order to represent the public and to make fair, publicly acceptable, and credible decisions.

There are a number of problems with this concept. There is, for example, no direct accountability to the public or constituent groups. HSAs mainly are accountable to federal project officers many layers down in the bureaucracy. Yet, to be effective, HSAs must have community credibility and acceptance. They are often strained by the pull of at least two masters (Berger, 1980).

The law's stipulation of governing board representation reflects a belief that the public interest will be served if all affected parties reach decisions and resolve differences through compromise. The law spells out which major demographic groups will be represented on the board, and precisely which providers must be included. Society is assumed to be composed of groups defined by shared economic, cultural, ethnic, and geographic interests, and that those are the legitimate interests in public policy formation (Lowi, 1964). There are conceptual and operational difficulties with this model, particularly the questions it raises about who represents the public and how the public interest is served (Vladeck, 1977).

---

*These are covered in detail by Morone in Volume Two.

One of the conceptual complications of this program is that consumers are expected to speak for their constituency with virtually no way of knowing its desires. As can be seen in legislatures and in labor negotiations, individuals speaking for groups of people seldom get complete accord with all other individuals in the group.

The law's stated assumptions about consumer participation were contrary to evidence concerning consumer or citizen participation. A hope that the problem of consumer participation was not structural rested on a belief that mediocre participation was caused by impediments and poor administration. If those were struck down and unenthusiastic implementation corrected, consumers would then participate as effectively and as actively as, for example, the providers. The "theory of concentrated interests" suggests that providers are active and "effective" on boards because their livelihoods and other professional rewards are directly involved. When one's interests are so clearly at stake, sustained effort is much more likely to take place (McConnell, 1967). Consumer advocates contended that their problems in representation and participation would be corrected by encouraging involvement of consumers with interests more directly tied to concerns about chronic disease or other special health problems. Selection of consumers by constituency groups tends to increase the individual consumer's sense of independence, confidence, and contribution to the planning process, and creates the advantages of "concentrated interests."

Governing Body Selection

The 1974 act was silent on selection procedures for board members and vague on the meaning of "broadly representative." By December 1977, the planning act was the subject of five lawsuits on the issue of consumer representation. In one of the most famous cases, *Texas ACORN*, the plaintiffs argued there were not enough poor consumers on the board and that, if people with higher incomes were supposed to represent lower-income consumers, the burden of proof was on the Health Systems Agency to indicate how the higher-income board members would do it.

The District Court of Appeals went further, requiring that DHHS demonstrate precisely how board members were representative of low-income or other demographically representative populations. This drew new attention to the selection process supposed to achieve substantive representation of demographic groups and groups concerned with specific diseases such as the American Cancer Society. It became evident that selection of HSA board members by organizations or groups outside the planning agencies was more likely to produce active representatives (Marmor and Morone, 1978). For example, the NAACP may now select an individual to represent blacks in the area. The board member is held accountable to the association, has a greater reason for involvement, and has access to a body of opinion, advice, resources, and staff to help do a more effective job.

Consumer groups, including the Public Citizen Health Research Group, the National Health Law Program, Georgia Legal Services, and the Consumer Coalition for Health, testified at various trials to many problems in the implementation of the consumer representation requirements. Witnesses documented instances of procedural gerrymandering; "elitist" self-selection; conflicts of interest; poor management, especially in relation to consumers; and violation of both the letter and the spirit of the law in some agencies. Although the number of documented cases was small, there was sufficient evidence of the need for more legislation and for pressure on DHHS to monitor the situation more closely (Fenerty, 1978; Georgia Legal Services, 1978).

The main consumer complaints concerned HSA board composition and representation, the process of selecting its members, and technical support for consumer representatives. The composition and representation question had been the subject of debate since 1974. The last two complaints were heard most often in the 1978 congressional hearings and in other recommendations from consumer groups and informed observers that preceded the 1979 amendments to the planning law.

The 1979 Amendments

DHHS had interpreted the 1974 act to call for a consumer majority selected almost by a quota system. The 1979 version was changed to read:

> The governing body must have a majority of consumers . . . who are *broadly representative* of

the health service area *and* shall include individuals representing the principal social,
economic, linguistic, handicapped, and racial
populations and geographic areas of the health
service area and major purchasers of health care
(including labor organizations and business corporations) in the area.

Perhaps most important in congressional hearings were
challenges to the selection of HSA governing body members.
The 1974 law was silent on the question, and the boards
were, in almost all cases, originally "self-selected."
Planning agencies, mostly private and nonprofit, incorporated themselves and applied to DHHS to be designated.
Critics argued that, no matter how well-intentioned,
self-selection at best ran the risk of in-group elitism
and a constricted view of the community and, at worst,
maintained control over decision making by those already
in positions of influence.

The 1979 amendments required a more open process for
the selection of governing body members, requiring
(1) that half of the members be selected by other methods
or people outside the existing governing body, (2) that
compositional requirements be met, (3) that there be
opportunity for broad community participation in selection, and (4) that community participation be encouraged
and facilitated.

Because of the organizational diversity of HSAs, the
Congress persisted in not prescribing a particular
method of board selection. It was hoped that the provisions of the amendments would ensure greater accountability to the public at large as well as to the constituent organization or group represented by an individual.*

The 1979 amendments also required a program of staff
support and education for governing body members. There
now has to be at least one agency staff member with
responsibility for assuring that governing body members,
especially consumers, get information and technical
assistance. Staff support was authorized on the assumption

---

*The House report for the proposed 1978 amendments had some
suggestions for methods, including appointment by organizations, or elected officials, selection by subarea councils,
selection by a membership corporation, and direct election.
This section was eliminated in 1979.

that consumer participation would be hampered by lack of health services expertise. Although consumers are seen as having a special contribution to make to the HSA because of their awareness of community needs and interests, the theme of the consumer as technically handicapped frequently recurs in health planning literature. The assignment of one staff person with consumer support responsibility is expected to improve the situation. For more discussion on this question, see Checkoway, Ellenburg, and Morone in Volume Two.

The 1974 statute had permitted reimbursement for reasonable costs incurred in attending meetings, and the report made clear that the purpose was to ensure participation of the economically disadvantaged. The 1979 amendments added the possibility of members receiving an advance for expenses, particularly important for low-income citizens.

Two specific interests were newly identified in 1979 as requiring representatives--the handicapped and mental health interests. Mental health can be represented by either a consumer or a provider.

Another modification in the HSA governing board was in the definition of a provider. Under the original act, a consumer representative who had been an employee or board member of a health center, hospital, or the like could not be a consumer representative on the board for at least 12 months. The amendments removed the 12-month exclusion, which had been a particular problem in sparsely settled areas and small towns.*

The 1979 amendments, which added purchasers to the definition of consumers, stated that they included, but were not limited to, unions and corporations. This was believed to be one method of strengthening the hands of consumers because purchasers are assumed to be knowledgeable about planning and have a vested interest in the outcome. Of unknown effect is a 1979 provision that government representatives can be either consumers or providers.

The legislative history of the 1979 amendments made suggestions for movement from the theoretically and operationally weak notion of descriptive representation

------

*There still is no precise policy on this question. Consumer members of hospital boards of trustees can be consumers for HSA purposes.

(as discussed by Morone in Volume Two of this study) toward a more practical concept of formal representation. The 1979 amendments opened up the selection process and strengthened the consumers' access to agency resources. Yet there remain a number of questions concerning consumer participation and how it might be made more effective. The balance of this chapter reports on the committee's findings and observations and concludes with its recommendations.

CURRENT ISSUES IN CONSUMER PARTICIPATION

The study committee held public hearings, commissioned several papers based on case studies, and collected data from the 1980 HSA applications for funding and designation. The problems revealed by these efforts are discussed in the several pages following.

Ambiguity of the Consumer's Role

Ambiguity of the consumer's role complicates evaluation of consumer participation. If it is perceived as a value and an end in itself, an evaluation would consist primarily of determining the number of participants and the frequency and intensity of their involvement. However, if participation is perceived as contributing to the attainment of explicitly stated goals, then an assessment of their effectiveness in terms of the particular goals needs to be undertaken (Marmor and Morone, 1978; Metsch and Veney, 1976; Rosenbaum, 1978; Rosener, 1978).

Whatever their intended purpose on HSA boards, consumers feel a disparity of role definition compared with providers. Many consumer groups argued that consumers act in isolation, without a well-defined constituency and without a clear perception of what they can hope to accomplish through their participatory efforts (Chavkin, 1980; Feinson, 1980; Paap, 1978).

Diversity of Opinion on Objectives

The objectives of consumer participation in health planning often are expressed as promoting provider responsiveness to the users of health care services; increasing consumer satisfaction; shaping changes in the health care system; improving the health status of the population; increasing efficiency and utilization of services; and the like (Koseki and Hayakawa, 1979). Yet the planning legislation defines consumers primarily by demographic characteristics and leaves unclear what the role of consumers is to be. Several observers have said that participation is a complex political notion, and there are more realistic ways to promote public participation than the methods mandated in the health planning legislation (Consumer Commission on the Accreditation of Health Services, Inc., 1978; Koseki and Hayakawa, 1979; Marmor and Morone, 1978; Metsch and Veney, 1976).

The vague statutory language concerning the objectives of consumer participation encourages a wide range of views as to what constitutes an effective consumer or effective consumer participation. Many consumer advocates describe effective consumers as speaking for the groups that provide them with organizational support and direction (Feinson, 1980; Knox, 1978; Marmor and Morone, 1978; Paap, 1978; Shannon, 1980), yet there is no consensus that an effective consumer member must have a constituency. However, there is agreement that effective participation requires that consumer values, preferences, needs, and perspectives substantially influence health planning.

The federal government's definition of consumer effectiveness probably would reflect a desire that consumers decrease the rate of growth in health care costs. Consumer representatives are asked to assist in cost control on the assumption they will reap some benefits. However, planning cannot guarantee that costs saved in one area (e.g., hospital utilization) will be available for other services. Maybe the provision of new and different services in one section of the system are dependent on controlling costs in other sections, but cost control may instead mean that the money saved will be spent outside the health sector. Some, including one consumer group, have argued that no one, and certainly not consumers by themselves, can effectively control costs in a health care system that has an economic base of fee-for-service reimbursement; private fiscal intermediaries; provider-controlled systems of accreditation, licensure, and quality control; and strong incentives for bringing more programs and services to local communities. Most of these influential factors are not under the control of planning agencies.

Others argue that providers would regard as effective those consumers who share provider values and support their decisions. Providers are most likely to resist demands for altering the present health care delivery system and historically have mobilized political and economic support to lobby for their interests (Colt, 1970; Lipsky and Lounds, 1976; Metsch and Veney, 1976).

Lack of Accountability and Appropriate Selection Processes

The health planning legislation's failure to provide for direct accountability of HSA governing board members is complicated by the differing definition of representation when applied to providers and consumers. A socially descriptive definition of representation is applied to consumers, but providers represent a group of specific health interests.

It has been argued that consumers should be selected by specific constituent organizations so they can be monitored and replaced if they are not adequately representing the interests of their constituency. However, Public Citizen Health Research Group (HRG) charged that in many areas there are inadequate consumer organizations from which to draw representatives. To compensate for this, the Health Research Group asserts that DHHS and the HSAs should be developing and funding consumer groups to feed into the planning process.

Twenty-eight percent of the agencies have provisions for the direct appointment of representatives by sources beyond the existing membership of the agency. However, few agencies surveyed (only 0.5 percent) annually asked constituent organizations to recertify that their appointees still represented their interests and thus remained "accountable." Fourteen percent of the agencies permit all governing body members to be directly appointed by local governmental authorities after appropriate solicitation of nominations from a broad range of sources. Such a process was regarded dubiously by one consumer group, which contended that local political systems have caused or perpetuated many of the difficulties in obtaining health care experienced by low-income persons.

Selection is inextricably linked to the problem of accountability, but timing was such that when the 1980

grant applications were being prepared* a majority of
HSAs (more than 51 percent) had not revised their selection processes to conform to the recent non-self-
perpetuating mandate.

Training Programs to Strengthen Consumers

The image of consumers as a weak voice in planning has
resulted in training programs to give them more of the
information that providers and planners have. Instead
of teaching consumers to apply their own values effectively, the programs try to train them in technical
planning. Some argue that a value approach is stronger
and more realistic than a technical approach. Although
the majority of HSAs have begun to implement the recent
legislative provisions that require an identifiable support program for board members, only 14 percent of
applications specifically mentioned an emphasis on
consumers.

Training programs for consumers have been limited by
inadequate resources (i.e., money, time, and materials).
Consumer activists mentioned the lack of training

---

*A review of all 1980 HSA grant applications revealed no
uniform election process. (By November 1980 only 19 percent of HSAs had selection processes approved by the
Bureau of Health Planning.) The selection processes may
be described in the following manner. Often a nominating
committee identified vacancies, defined the categories
of membership required to maintain representational compliance, and solicited (through the media or from a file
of potential members) nominations from a variety of
sources. Upon receipt of the nominations, a matrix desig-
nating the appropriate category for each nominee was
prepared, and a slate of nominees, along with the nominating
committee's recommendations, was forwarded to the governing
body for their election. When more than one interested
organization wished to represent a membership category,
a cluster group of related organizations was established
to select a representative. Fourteen percent of the HSAs
permitted all members to be directly appointed by public
elected officials, and 2 percent reported election
processes conducted by mail.

resources at the consumers' disposal (i.e., special
funds, staff, time, etc.) as contributing to consumers'
inability to sustain their work as community representatives. On the other hand, others noted that many providers need training in issues in the consumers' bailiwick,
and other fields, particularly innovative methods of
health service delivery and financing. All agree that it
is important that information be provided in a concise
and manageable form for everyone's sake.

Sources of Tension and Costs of Consumer Participation

Consumers' tensions arise because of their ambiguous roles.
Consumer representatives feel powerless because insufficient technical and financial resources are devoted to
making them effective participants. In order to be
effective, consumer representatives must expend time,
effort, and money. Time and effort must be devoted to
(a) attending meetings, hearings, and workshops,
(b) responding to questionnaires and being interviewed,
(c) writing letters to officials, securing information
about issues, digesting materials provided by agency
staff, and participating in advisory bodies. Monetary
costs arise in time lost from a job, travel, child care,
telephone calls, and similar matters, all of which pose
special hardships for low-income, elderly, and handicapped consumers. There are also the psychological costs
of frustration, slow movement of even the smoothest
planning process, and the lag in time between effort and
results. As the costs rise, so does the number of citizens excluded from participation or unwilling to participate. The term "burn out" it used often to describe
board members' and staff members' feelings about their
efforts and their frustrations, especially when the
federal government applies new requirements without
understanding, sympathy, or appreciation, at least as it
is viewed from the field.

FINDINGS AND RECOMMENDATIONS

Consumer Participation

The committee found that the health planning program
is an enterprise aimed, among other goals, at more

broadly distributing political power for advising on an
area's health resources. Health planning attempts to
remove decision-making from provider domination and give
the public more influence. By specifically naming certain types of consumers to be represented, the planning
act invited participation by groups historically ill-
served by the health system. *The committee concludes
that an important contribution of the program is the
addition to the advisory process of consumers, particularly those who represent the traditionally underserved and
underrepresented.*

The consumer role will become even more important as
fiscal problems lead to the need for decisions about
what will be supported or not. Reductions in services
are not likely to fall evenly on all citizens. Planning
agencies can gather information, expose inequities, and
help the public understand the long-term social and
economic consequences of cutbacks in services.

It is unlikely that in times of rapid inflation and
cutbacks in almost all services that low-income and
minority citizens, who are frequently politically powerless, will have many opportunities for ensuring that
their needs have high priority. The health planning
agencies can make a special effort to find new, imaginative ways to adapt resources to provide services that are
needed but not available. These should include, but
not be limited to, serving the aged, children, and the
deinstitutionalized mentally ill and mentally retarded.

The committee found the role of consumers in planning
agencies to be ambiguous. A major source of ambiguity is
that it is not clear whether consumers should "mirror"
the community as a whole, and, as a consequence, speak for
it, or represent particular constituencies. In practice
there is a mixture of such models of representation. Few
consumers formally represent constituency groups, but
many providers do.

The legislative history of the 1979 amendments suggests
a model of board composition that somewhat moves away from
the mirror view embodied in the 1974 act and toward more
connections to interest groups.

The concepts of a consumer majority in health planning
and planning as an arena for multiple-interest bargaining are widely accepted. But questions will continue
to arise about which interests are to be represented,
who will speak for those interests, and how the individuals
are selected and held accountable.

Many perceive consumers and providers as natural
enemies, with the HSA an arena for combat. Others fear
the possible loss of the originally conceived structure
in which citizens and professionals could plan for
health services in a cooperative manner.

Those who view the HSA as a carefully structured
locus for adversarial interchange and achievement of
hard-fought compromise are concerned that the consumers
have sufficient assistance to offset the providers'
advantages of resources and expertise. There will continue to be demands for staff, special training, and
networks of information for consumers.

There are some who would like an all-consumer board,
with providers serving as technical advisers,* but this
idea is far different from that institutionalized in
1974, which sought to balance consumer and provider
interests.

There are advantages to having consumers selected by,
and responsible to, constituency or interest groups.
There is evidence that representatives of groups are more
effective participants in the planning program, and it is
in the interest of the program to have confident and
active consumers.

*But the committee saw both advantages and disadvantages
to a pluralist, interest group bargaining model. For
example, while participation and accountability are enhanced, heightened conflict may weaken the ability of the
board to find cooperative solutions to problems. Of
particular concern to this committee is how the public
interest is represented in the process.*

The committee discussed several approaches, including
one that many agencies now use, in which some proportion
of the consumers are selected by and represent different
organizations and interests, and others are elected or
appointed "at large" or by public officials.

*The committee found that there are solid arguments
for not making radical changes in methods of governing
body selection and composition.* Many of the planning
agencies already are engaged in altering those procedures

---

*The British have advisory community health councils com-
posed of citizens, with the possibility of a doctor being
the citizen representative if selected to speak for a
group of consumers.

to conform with the 1979 amendments. The agencies need time to regroup and build their capabilities. Further changes should be avoided until experience has been gathered on the 1979 changes.

The results of the changed requirements have created a nation full of natural experiments with substantial diversity that can be used to improve our understanding of the factors that encourage effective consumer participation. *The committee recommends that the Health Resources Administration take advantage of the diversity in the nation to evaluate different approaches to board selection, composition, and methods of fostering active participation.* It will be particularly important that such evaluations be academically defensible to ensure that changes considered in 1982 be based on solid data.

The committee does not think that a requirement for more formal links with constituency groups is currently warranted. Existing groups can be used to informally strengthen citizen involvement and understanding of health planning. The attributes of clearly defined constituencies, experience in organizational politics, and resources can be used by individual board members.

The task at hand is to overcome political imbalance within the HSA governing body to ensure that planning agencies satisfactorily address a wide range of community concerns. If this goal is achieved, board composition becomes less important. Questions concerning the purposes of participation arise anew. Is the participation of consumers so highly valued that when agencies face budget cuts the costs of consumer participation are still justifiable?

More questions about the aims of the 1974 legislation and its citizen participation model will arise with each significant modification in the program. The expectation that the HSA governing body would include individuals able to initiate change and members of the community's power structure to ensure implementation of planning decisions has receded. Instead, the governing bodies are often viewed as an arena for competing interests to resolve differences.

The governing board model of today is still a mirror view, but with consumers strengthened by connections with organizations with certain special interests represented. This is different from the previous concept of a mixture of providers and nonprovider citizens, including some of the community's leaders and change agents. Whether or not

this shift will make the planning program less connected
to the loci of power, and thus less influential, is not
clear.

There are advantages to having a highly public advisory
process in which all of the key interests and perspectives
in health matters must operate. Making public both technical issues and questions of value and judgment ensures
the negotiations are in the public interest.

The committee recommends against changes in the
selection and composition of governing bodies at this
time. The committee did not find any demonstrably better
approach to enhancing consumer participation, but it
uncovered some approaches to reduce impediments to more
effective citizen activism.

*The committee recommends that the DHHS identify
and disseminate methods for enhancing participation in
HSA governance, especially by consumers.* Methods
described in Volume Two by Checkoway and Morone should
be circulated widely. Good examples that might be cited
as models include the Northern Virginia HSA and the West
Bay HSA.

Education should not be limited to consumers. Providers also need to learn about innovative and alternative
service delivery, the importance of health promotion and
disease prevention, consumer values, health economics,
and the application of epidemiology to health planning.
Training should cover many of these matters, as well as
methods of decision-making, leadership, and conflict
resolution that can be employed by governing boards.

The Health Resources Administration should explore
possibilities for enhancing consumer participation. For
example, caucuslike activities might be fostered to give
consumers the kind of psychological support that other
board members get from their professional, peer, and occupational roles. Consumers might establish the agenda
for their own training. But attention to consumers
should not detract from the importance of a combination
of providers and consumers on the boards, and the support
that providers can and do give to consumers. As Checkoway
noted (Volume Two): ". . . providers were sometimes more
outspoken than their consumer counterparts in favor of
consumer interests."

The function of the consumer as spokesperson for
certain values and points of view is important. Consumers
often will not want to become "technical" planners.
Rather they will wish to maintain the primacy of their

values and opinions in a complicated technical and
political process. They will sometimes need more technical information to effectively interject their values
into the process, and there should be reasonable availability of technical support when they want it.

The committee debated whether or not consumer board
members should be paid for their participation. Providers, professionals, and public officials often participate as part of their jobs or related to their
professional/career interests. Many of the problems of
consumer participation might be reduced if citizens were
paid for some documented preparation time and for attendance at governing body meetings and public hearings.

The committee recognizes certain advantages to
reimbursement for participation, but does not feel that
a recommendation in favor of that idea is appropriate
at this time.

First, payment only to lower-income members would
require a "means test," which was unacceptable to
everyone on the committee. Second, the program's
voluntary nature is considered important. Third, the
costs would be enormous and could absorb a major part
of the budget of some agencies.

The committee also discussed a possible recommendation
that consumers have their own staff to counterbalance
the advantages of providers and their board members.

In general the committee concludes that it needs to
know much more about the dynamics of the staff support
issue. The committee applauded the changes made by the
1979 amendments and suggestions in the legislative history
aimed at strengthening consumers through staff support.
It is evident that consumers seem to be more effective
when they have developed good relationships with staff.
Governing bodies should recognize the importance of
this support and make certain that board and staff
relationships are appropriately structured and, in
particular, that consumers feel confident in their roles.
But the committee also noted the divisive potential of
having separate staff members reporting to the consumers
only. In general, the HSA board should clearly understand
its policymaking role and its "supervisory" relationship
to the executive director who serves at its pleasure.
Staff must bear in mind their position (under the authority
of the executive director) as staff to the governing body.
Consumers need to understand that as majority members of
the governing bodies, they are supposed to be in a strong

position, particularly in setting policy and determining
the overall agency management style through hiring and
control of the executive director. Difficulties with
the nature and quality of staff support should be worked
out with the director.

To develop assistance for consumer representatives,
the board can authorize special funds for use by consumers. Such funds could be used to hire experts, conduct research, organize meetings, and consult with local
consumer and professional interests, obtain administrative
and support services, and the like.

These recommendations draw on mixed evidence concerning
consumer participation. In Volume Two, Morone, Checkoway,
and others report strength and toughness among some consumers and more division among providers than was anticipated. Much of the difference between theory and the
evidence might be attributable to an underestimation of
the role of staff. Morone found, for example, that staff
served "to balance the concentrated stakes of provider
representatives." Checkoway, too, highlighted the pivotal
role of staff attitudes in facilitating consumer involvement.

It is particularly interesting that Checkoway, among
others, notes a growing capacity and increasing number
of citizens who understand health issues and are actively
trying to achieve their goals.

The committee also discussed the possibility of
recommending requirements for more insurers and third-
party payors on governing bodies. Some of the committee
felt strongly that third-party payors, insurers, and
other major health services purchasers should play major
roles in health planning. Others felt equally strongly
that more formal involvement of insurers, third-party
payors, and purchasers would be a mistake. The base
for opinion and judgment was inadequate for the committee
to take a stand, although Sapolsky in Volume Two takes
a clear position on that topic.

To conclude, *the committee decided that there was a
need for experiments and rigorously designed studies to
learn about factors that contribute to effective consumer participation.* There was ample opinion and speculation, but the knowledge base is flabby and mixed. Chapter 3 discusses the importance of administrative flexibility to allow experiments to be undertaken.

*The committee concludes that the area of consumer
participation needs systematic study and attention and*

the Health Resources Administration should help foster such experiments.

Locations in which there are strong links between planning decisions and third-party payment should be studied. Locations where the board includes a larger proportion of payors, insurers, or purchasers should also be studied to see whether or not there are differences in the effectiveness of these agencies.

5 SUMMARY OF FINDINGS AND RECOMMENDATIONS

This concluding chapter reiterates the findings and recommendations of the committee, and summarizes the most important supporting discussions from Chapters 2, 3, and 4 of this volume.

SELECTED ISSUES IN HEALTH PLANNING

At the end of this second year of the study, the committee reaffirms its first year's finding that the current health planning program has substantial potential for helping to achieve certain important social goals, through local planning for improved local health care systems.

In general, the health planning program in the United States may be characterized as a citizen-dominated trusteeship in the field of health. At its best and at its most inspiring theoretical level, it may be seen as a new institution charged with helping to ensure that individual institutions or actors will promote, or at least not adversely affect, the development of a health care system that provides for all the citizenry "access to quality health care at reasonable cost." Like all of our social institutions, when operating and viewed up close, the picture is sometimes less inspiring, and suffers from human failures. As always, there are problems in devising arrangements and methods for structuring the unusual American institution that is health planning. In particular, the committee wishes to encourage much more flexibility in administration and, where local communities desire it, experimentation. The intentionally decentralized process for planning and resources development should be viewed as an opportunity for learning how to help deploy health resources in this country.

Expectations for planning agencies must be consistent
with the tools provided them. Too often, the local and
state health planning agencies become the arena for
attempts to resolve federal or national problems, but the
resources and authorities necessary for resolving such
problems remain outside the local agencies' control.
Similarly, federal administrators tend to look at the
broad mandate given planning and assign new responsibilities, ignoring the limited authority and resources of the
agencies.

Observers have also noted federal direction that is
inconsistent with the Congress' expressed desire to
decentralize the health planning and resource allocation
process, placing a community's health destiny in its own
hands. It would be logical to assume that a program with
the structural complexity and breadth of responsibility
of the health planning program would create divergent
expectations at the various levels involved. The committee found this to be the case.

Not surprisingly, given variations in perceived program
goals, changes in the political and social environment,
and shifting demands on the agencies, the "successes"
attributed to health planning have been limited, and dissatisfaction with the program has been expressed. The
committee believes that the program deserves time to
mature and to be evaluated with measures consistent both
with its mission and its resources. To date, evaluation
has focused almost exclusively on capital expenditure
control. But the planning program was not intended to be a
major cost containment device and it lacks the authority
needed to effectively control expenditures. That the results have been less than desired should surprise nobody.
Rather than focusing on narrowly defined planning goals,
the planning system should be viewed as an important,
somewhat experimental effort toward forming relationships
among agencies of government, between the public and private sectors, and between the processes of politics
and technology. The HSAs should be evaluated as to whether
they fulfill criteria of a democratic process, including
fairness, openness, potential for participation, and the
extent to which they employ data and information appropriately. Health planning also, when it works well, is
an inherently political process. That must also be kept
in mind when evaluating the program. Failure to do so
may lead to incorrect, and even damaging, conclusions concerning the program's effectiveness. To judge the program

by theoretical standards of rational decision-making
would be inappropriate.

Built-in limitations on effectiveness of the planning
program are sometimes overlooked by critics. Naive
expectations persist about what is possible for the health
planning network. It was assigned a lofty and laudable
but difficult set of goals; that is, to assist in "the
achievement of equal access to quality health care at a
reasonable cost." It was intentionally not given any real
budgetary or regulatory powers by which to accomplish
these goals. It was asked to focus on objectives that
are often contradictory, such as improving health
status and controlling costs.

As is often the case in U.S. politics, a crisis
atmosphere and inflated promises accompanied the passage
of the planning act. The committee believes that there
is a need to scale-down the unrealistic expectations for
the health planning program. The political process seems
to require rhetoric and overselling in order to maintain
a coalition. The committee feels that the effect of
the overselling is not neutral. It fosters skepticism
about our nation's ability to solve problems and discourages faith in any government action.

If the program is not living up to all of the expectations of the various interests involved in its design
and operation, the committee observed that a problem may
be with the expectations, rather than the program itself.

The committee concluded that the demonstrated differences between the goals professed in the act and those applied by federal administrators and the Congress in evaluation may lead to invalid conclusions concerning the program's continuation. The committee recommends that a
clearer statement of purposes and expectations of the
health planning program be developed as a basis for evaluation of its effectiveness. This statement should recognize the limitations imposed on the program by its level of
funding and authority, and provide better direction to
both levels concerning the program's activities. Clearly
developed goals and expectations should protect the
planning program from criticism that results from conflicting values and changing priorities.

It is the committee's judgment that the purposes of the
program for which the program could be and should be held
accountable, in the order of their importance, based in
the program's nature and authority, are:

1. To establish and maintain an open, participatory
structure for articulating community health needs and
desirable alternatives for meeting those needs, to be
used in advising both governmental and private sector
decision-makers who control health resources at the local,
state, and national levels.
2. To contribute to the redirection of the health
system through planning for a more effective, accessible,
higher-quality, and more efficient configuration of
facilities and services that is more closely matched to
basic health care needs of an area's population. This
should include developing a carefully thought-out position
for dealing with the introduction of new technological
advances into the health care system, with sensitive consideration and fair-minded appraisal of all important
factors, not only costs. Done properly, this purpose
should lead to a contribution in the overall containment
in the rise of health expenditures, so this purpose and
the next one (3) are not truly separable. However,
specifying a cost containment mission, as well, within
the proper context, is important to ensure that the
committee is not misunderstood.
3. To contribute to the "containment of health care
costs," that is, to contribute to moderation in the rise
of health care expenditures, primarily through planning a
more cost-effective health system as discussed in (2),
through efforts to improve the health status of the population, especially through programs that promote health and
prevent disease, and efforts to limit unnecessary capital
investment and direct such investment toward most cost-
effective facilities and services.

It is important that this use of "cost containment"
not be confused with budget cuts for health and social
services, particularly for low-income, old, and disabled
citizens. A more cost-effective health system that meets
the requirements of citizens can be achieved through
improvements in the deployment of technology and high-cost
services. Planning is aimed at a better match between
requirements and services, not at cutting out the services
for which reimbursement is currently inadequate.
These purposes are directed at improving the health of
the people, the overriding goal of the planning system.
However, given the sometimes indirect link between changes
in health services and incremental improvements in health
status, and the difficulty in measuring such changes in

the short term and attributing such changes to the health
planning agencies' actions, it is unreasonable to judge
the program on short-term health status changes in the
areas' or states' population.

A major interest of the committee was to call for a
fair, realistic evaluation of the health planning program in terms of the systems that it was intended to
affect, not just the nation as a whole. In effect, while
the program is aimed at making an overall difference in
the way that health resources are deployed in this
country, any fair evaluation of the program must be disaggregated. Planning is a national investment and a
fair question to ask is whether or not this is a good
public investment by the federal government. But, the
answer must be reached by looking at the achievements of
many different areas and whether or not the respective
publics are benefitting from this planning.

Agreement is needed on the definition of national
interest as it relates to health planning and on what
level of return for the planning investment is acceptable.
Given the size and diversity of the nation, the evidence
will be mixed. Trends and overall findings will be the
only evidence concerning what is happening.

To summarize, the committee believes that it is
important to state what can reasonably be expected and
to assess program performance against that standard.
The health planning program cannot accomplish all that
political rhetoric has demanded of it. The critical
questions, however, are what can it reasonably be expected
to accomplish? Would those accomplishments, if achieved,
warrant continuation of the program? And are those goals
being achieved? This committee has concluded that the
health planning program cannot be expected, by itself,
to resolve the various difficulties that the American
health sector faces. It believes, however, that the
program can make a contribution toward such resolution.
Even the more limited objectives and expectations are
worth pursuing.

NATIONAL, STATE, AND LOCAL ROLES AND RELATIONSHIPS

The complex health planning structure that has evolved
over the past 30 years is the result of many disparate
factors. These include: (1) the fragmented, diversely
controlled health enterprise that contains public agencies

engaged in financing, regulating, and delivering traditional public health services that in turn coexist with a substantial voluntary system for delivering similar services;
(2) an historical resistance to "planning" in this country;
(3) conflicting interests of national, state, and local
actors in the planning arena, each with their own notions
of the degree to which planning should be centralized or
decentralized; and (4) political processes and compromises
necessary in this country to produce legislation.

Given such complexity, it is hardly surprising that
testimony before the committee included dissatisfaction
with the planning program. The major areas of concern
and committee recommendations follow.

Relationships with Federal Medical Care Systems

The medical care systems owned and operated by the federal
government are significant elements in the total health
care resources available to the nation. Federal beneficiaries and resources should be considered as part of the
community health planning process, and planners for the
federal system will undoubtedly want to take into account
an area's total resources when planning for that eligible
population.

The committee encourages more dialogue in these matters
and actions that will create the most cost-effective health
system for all citizens, including those to whom the
federal government has obligations.

*Recommendations to Expand Coverage of the Planning
Program*

The committee found the relatively low level of linkages
between planning and financing to be a major barrier to
achieving the goals of the health planning legislation.
In the committee's view, strengthening linkages between
health planning and the reimbursement system should be a
high priority for study and for experimental programs
within selected states. Such linkages might take the
form of a tie between reimbursement under federal programs
and findings that services reimbursed are appropriately
organized and offered in accord with the plans, criteria,
and standards developed and applied by the health planning
agencies. Expanded efforts to link planning and state rate

review programs should be fostered by the federal government so that the most effective models can be identified.

The Congress explicitly required health planning agencies to implement plans to regionalize health services and reduce redundant services. But the legislation contained no explicit exemption from antitrust legislation for planning activities undertaken by providers. The issue has since been raised in the courts. The threat of antitrust action still hangs over some implementation efforts.

The committee endorses the concept of an explicit antitrust exemption for activities publicly undertaken by providers in conjunction with health systems agencies, and in accord with the goals, objectives, and recommended actions as embodied in duly adopted health systems plans. The committee recognized that the issues involved in granting such an exemption are complex, and that the exemption language must be carefully structured to prevent abuse. In order to define the issues more carefully, and to develop the most useful legislative language, the committee recommends that the National Council on Health Planning and Development, working with the Department of Justice and the Federal Trade Commission, establish a task force to develop proposed legislative language. As long as the threat of antitrust action casts a shadow over efforts to secure change through cooperative actions, the pressure will mount to apply regulatory solutions where nonregulatory action would work equally as well. The committee hopes that the council will move expeditiously to begin this important task.

Recommendations Concerning Agency Diversity

The committee heard testimony suggesting "overmanagement" by the federal administrative agency, and a greater emphasis on achieving program compliance than on providing assistance to enhance program effectiveness.

The planning statute is unusually detailed, yet extensive regulations, program policies, and guidelines have been issued. The committee believes that administrative attention might better be directed to fostering diversity in approaches used by the agencies (within the broad constraints of the legislation) and to studying the results than to efforts to achieve a high degree of uniformity through inflexibly applied supplemental regulations. The operation of this program could provide an opportunity to learn and observe what works well or poorly under different conditions. The committee recommends that the federal administrators of the program adopt a policy of promoting or allowing natural experiments in both agency structure and in methods for carrying out agency responsibilities, and study the results. Such "experiments" already exist within the constraints of the statute. The committee feels that even more flexibility is needed to learn about how to accommodate to local conditions. Trial of some alternative approaches to agency organizations and operation will not be possible without changes in legislation. The committee believes that to enable such experiments to be performed, Congress, in reauthorizing the planning program, should make explicit its interest in allowing experimental approaches to test different ways of health services planning and locally designed methods for advising on the deployment of health resources, especially new technology. The current "controlling" approach to administration being pursued by the federal administration denies the federal government, state government, and localities the opportunity to learn while doing, essential in any complex program, but especially one aimed at creating local institutions.

The choices of experiments should be made by the planning agencies, according to size of grant, composition of staff, and priorities and interests of the governing body and the state. These recommendations will require more flexibility than program administrators have permitted in the past.

The committee also recommends that some agencies be better funded to test and document possible effects of planning with greater funding. In some cases, the required supplemental money might come from third-party payors. In addition, some agencies should be allowed extra Area Health Services Development Funds for seed money to help get projects started.

The Congress must make explicit its interest in genuine experimentation in how to effect change to find the best ways to conduct planning. Contrary to the more usual uniform federal approach to problems, a major goal of this program would be to encourage variation and diversity to learn more about the optimal methods for allocating resources.

Experimentation in Reimbursement and Capital Controls

Clearly, reimbursement programs that simply accept or pass through land, plant, and equipment costs as reasonable and necessary encourage investment, and because of their limited authority, CON and 1122 programs cannot, on their own, effectively control costs.

The committee finds that creative reimbursement approaches and new methods to limit nonessential or excessive capital investment are long overdue. The Congress should enact enabling legislation and authorize funds to monitor and evaluate such experiments. There are a wide range of approaches that could be considered, such as:

· state setting an aggregate limit on capital purchase in health over a 3-5-year period;
· state rate regulators imposing per-case reimbursement limits, or studying the experience with this reimbursement in New Jersey;
· federal reimbursement experiments that limit paying for interest, depreciating rent, and other land costs.
· federal or state efforts to limit the supply of private loan financing to hospitals or nursing homes.

Recommendations for Stability and Funding

The health structure is an enduring one, and health planning agencies are at a disadvantage in working from a base of 3-year authorizations. By placing the planning and control system at risk every 3 years, the Congress erodes its potential effectiveness. In the committee's view, longer authorization periods would help planning maintain the commitment and interest of its volunteers and combat resistance to change in the communities.

Accordingly, the committee recommends that the Congress take the steps necessary to provide a greater degree of temporal and fiscal stability to the program. Among the considerations that should enter into development of improved legislation are the length of program authorization, the possibility of developing a stable financial base through use of a trust fund approach for at least a portion of the funding, and the use of guaranteed future funding to enable agencies to budget more effectively.

The committee explored the potential for alternative
funding sources for health planning, and particularly for
HSAs. The committee concluded that funding at the local
level by interested parties raised potential conflicts of
interest, or the appearance of such conflicts. The
possibility of influence was also a factor which makes
unwise the use of money from providers or third-party
payors, particularly if provided on a voluntary rather
than mandatory basis. The committee could not reach
agreement on how funding for the planning agencies might
be broadened without putting other goals, such as planning
agency independence, at risk. But the committee felt
strongly that any actions by the federal government based
on an assumption that state and local governments or
others would pick up funding would be illusory at best.

The committee recommends that the National Council on
Health Planning and Development undertake a special study
of the planning agency funding issue, with the goal of
producing recommendations for consideration by the
Congress during the 1982 review of the authorizing
legislation.

Recommendations About Relationships Among Agencies

A particular set of relationship problems for states
with a single HSA were reported. In such states, where
the population and resource base is not sufficient to support multiple HSAs, concerns were expressed concerning
potential and actual duplication of efforts between the
HSA and SHPDA. The committee decided that special
attention should be given to dividing functions and
responsibilities so as to eliminate duplication or waste.
It was concerned that eliminating agencies or turning them
into 1536 entities might create problems of access to the
agency, especially by consumers, and reduce opportunity
for citizen involvement. Because citizen participation
is one of the strengths of the planning program, it would
be undesirable to constrict it too much in the name of
system efficiency.

At the local level, the health planning structure has
an array of horizontal relationships with both governmental and nongovernmental organizations. The range of
organizations whose involvement facilitates the planning
process is broad. Among the most important of these
relationships from the perspective of the committee are

those with local official health agencies that are not
directly required to deal with the planning agencies.
An expanding interest in prevention and health promotion
should help to enlist health planning agencies in such
activities. Local and state health departments have the
major operating responsibility in these areas. They are
a repository of expertise that should be engaged in
planning for such efforts.

The committee concludes that closer operating relationships between health planning and official health agencies
should be promoted. This does not require that health
planning be conducted by governmental organizations, but
rather than such organizations be involved in planning.

Other important relationships are those among planning
agencies and other federally supported regional bodies.
Such bodies, particularly PSROs, collect data and conduct
activities that are directly related to improvement of
the quality of care, also a concern of health planning.
The committee recognizes the differences between the
missions of the PSROs and the planning bodies and the
real problems that exist concerning data confidentiality.
In fact, the committee felt that there is too much attention paid to their working together when their tasks are
quite different and the real opportunities for working
together are limited.

The committee recommends that the National Professional
Standards Review Council and the National Council on
Health Planning and Development jointly develop a position
concerning data and other information exchange that meets
the legitimate need for such data for health planning
purposes while observing legitimate concerns regarding
confidentiality of individual patient data.

CONSUMER PARTICIPATION

The planning act of 1974 mandated that HSA governing
boards contain a majority of consumer representatives.
The intention was to ensure that consumer preferences,
values, and interests would be voiced in the planning
arena. It was hoped that numerical superiority of consumers would balance the greater concentration of interests, resources, and political and technical sophistica-
tion of provider board members. But consumer participation
in health planning has been viewed by many as ineffective.
Amendments to the planning act in 1979 tried to rectify

some of the problems, but other problems remain. The committee examined a number of issues related to consumer participation. The major topics examined were: ambiguity in the role of consumers, questions of accountability, and training to strengthen consumer effectiveness.

The committee found that the health planning program is an enterprise aimed, among other goals, at more broadly distributing political power for advising on an area's health resources. Health planning attempts to remove decision-making from provider domination and give the public more influence. The committee concluded that an important contribution of the program is the addition to the advisory process of consumers, particularly those who represent the traditionally underserved and underrepresented.

The consumer role will become even more important as fiscal problems lead to the need for decisions about what health services will be supported. Reductions in services are not likely to fall evenly on all citizens.

The health planning agencies, with their carefully constituted governing bodies, can make a special effort, working with providers, to pool their skills and capacities to find new imaginative ways to adapt resources to unattended health needs and ensure that the underserved and politically powerless remain priorities. These should include but not be limited to the aged, children, and the deinstitutionalized mentally ill and mentally retarded.

The committee found the role of consumers in planning agencies to be ambiguous. A major source of ambiguity is that it is not clear whether consumers should "mirror" the community as a whole, and, as a consequence, speak for it, or represent particular constituencies. In practice, there is a mixture of such models of representation. Few consumers formally represent constituency groups, but many providers do. Questions remain about which consumer interests should be represented, by whom, and how such representatives are to be selected and held accountable.

But the committee saw both advantages and disadvantages to a pluralist, interest group bargaining model. For example, while participation and accountability are enhanced, heightened conflict may weaken the ability of the board to find cooperative solutions to problems. Of particular concern to this committee is how the public interest is represented in the process.

The committee discussed several approaches, including one that many agencies now use, in which some proportion of the consumers are selected by and represent different organizations and interests, and others are elected or appointed "at large" or by public officials.

The committee found that there are solid arguments for not making radical changes in methods of governing body selection and composition. Many of the planning agencies already are engaged in altering those procedures to conform with the 1979 amendments. The agencies need time to regroup and build their capabilities. Further changes should be avoided until experience has been gathered on the 1979 changes.

The results of the changed requirements have created a nation full of natural experiments with substantial diversity that can be used to improve our understanding of the factors that encourage effective consumer participation. The committee recommends that the Health Resources Administration take advantage of the diversity in the nation to evaluate different approaches to board selection, composition and methods of fostering active participation. It will be particularly important that such evaluations be academically defensible to ensure that changes considered in 1982 be based on solid data.

The committee does not think that a requirement for more formal links with constituency groups is currently warranted. Existing groups can be used to informally strengthen citizen involvement and understanding of health planning. The attributes of clearly defined constituencies, experience in organizational politics, and resources can be used by individual board members.

The task at hand is to overcome political imbalance within the HSA governing body to ensure that planning agencies satisfactorily address a wide range of community concerns. If this goal is achieved, board composition becomes of less importance. Questions concerning the purposes of participation arise anew. Is the participation of consumers so highly valued that when agencies face budget cuts the costs of consumer participation are still justifiable?

Some advantages of the public advisory process that involves all key interests are the public discussion of both technical issues and questions of value and judgment.

Education should not be limited to consumers. Providers also need to learn about innovative and alternative service delivery, the importance of health promotion and

disease prevention, consumer values, health economics,
and the application of epidemiology to health planning.
Training should cover many of these matters, as well as
methods of decision-making, leadership, and conflict
resolution that can be employed by governing boards.

The Health Resources Administration should explore
possibilities for enhancing consumer participation. For
example, caucuslike activities might be fostered to give
consumers the kind of psychological support that other
board members get from their professional, peer, and
occupational roles. Consumers might establish the agenda
for their own training. But attention to consumers should
not detract from the importance of a combination of providers and consumers on the boards, and the support that
providers can and do give to consumers. As Checkoway
noted: ". . . providers were sometimes more outspoken than
their consumer counterparts in favor of consumer interests."

The function of the consumer as spokesperson for certain
values and points of view is important. Consumers often
will not want to become "technical" planners. Rather
they will wish to maintain the primacy of their values
and opinions in a complicated technical and political
process. They will sometimes need more technical information to effectively interject their values into the
process, and there should be reasonable availability of
technical support when they want it.

The committee debated whether or not consumer board
members should be paid for their participation. Providers, professionals, and public officials often participate as part of their jobs or in relation to their
professional/career interests. Many of the problems of
consumer participation might be reduced if citizens
were paid for some documented preparation time and for
attendance at governing body meetings and public
hearings.

The committee recognizes certain advantages to reimbursement for participation, but does not feel that a
recommendation in favor of that idea is appropriate at
this time.

First, payment only to lower-income members would
require a "means test," which was unacceptable to everyone on the committee. Second, the program's voluntary
nature is considered important. Third, the costs would
be enormous, and could absorb a major part of the budget
of some agencies.

The committee also discussed a possible recommendation that consumers have their own staff to counterbalance the advantages of providers and other board members.

In general the committee concludes that it needs to know much more about the dynamics of the staff support issue. The committee applauded the changes made by the 1979 amendments and suggestions in the legislative history aimed at strengthening consumers through staff support. It is evident that consumers seem to be more effective when they have developed good relationships with staff. Governing bodies should recognize the importance of this support and make certain that board and staff relationships are appropriately structured and, in particular, that consumers feel confident in their roles. But the committee also noted the divisive potential of having separate staff members reporting to the consumers only. In general, the HSA board should clearly understand its policymaking role and its "supervisory" relationship to the executive director who serves at its pleasure. Staff must bear in mind their position (under the authority of the executive director) as staff to the governing body. Consumers need to understand that as majority members of the governing bodies, they are supposed to be in a strong position, particularly in setting policy and determining the overall agency management style through hiring and control of the executive director. Difficulties with the nature and quality of staff support should be worked out with the director.

To develop assistance for consumer representatives, the board can authorize special funds for use by consumers. Such funds could be used to hire experts, conduct research, organize meetings, and consult with local consumer and professional interests, obtain administrative and support services, and the like.

The committee also discussed the possibility of recommending requirements for more insurers and third-party payors on governing bodies. Some of the committee felt strongly that third-party payors, insurers, and other major health services purchasers should play major roles in health planning. Others felt equally strongly that more formal involvement of insurers, third-party payors, and purchasers would be a mistake. The base for opinion and judgment was inadequate for the committee to take a stand, although Sapolsky in Volume Two takes a clear position on that topic.

To conclude, the committee decided that there was a need for experiments and rigorously designed studies to learn about factors that contribute to effective consumer participation. There is ample opinion and speculation, but the knowledge base is flabby and mixed. Chapter 3 discusses the importance of administrative flexibility to allow experiments to be undertaken.

The committee concludes that the area of consumer participation needs systematic study and attention and the Health Resources Administration should help foster such experiments.

Locations in which there are strong links between planning decisions and third-party payment should be studied. Locations where the board includes a larger proportion of payors, insurers, or purchasers should also be studied to see whether or not there are differences in the effectiveness of these agencies.

REFERENCES

Bauer, Katherine G. "The Arranged Marriage of Health Planning and Regulation for Cost Containment Under P.L. 93-641--Some Issues to be Faced." *Harvard University Center for Community Health and Medical Care Report*. Series R58-1, December 1977.

Bell, James B. "Rapid Feedback Evaluation Report One: Prototype Telephone Surveys for HSA Impact Monitoring." Washington, D.C.: The Urban Institute, 1978.

Berger, Sally. "The National Health Planning Program." Presentation to the National Council on Health Planning and Development, Subcommittee on Implementation and Administration, June 12, 1980.

Cain, Harry P., II, and Darling (Thornberry), Helen N. "Health Planning in the United States: Where We Stand Today." *Health Policy and Education* 1(1979):5-25.

Caper, S. Philip. Personal Communication, Washington, D.C., March 1980.

Chavkin, David. Testimony on behalf of the National Health Law Program, before the Institute of Medicine, Committee on Health Planning, Goals and Standards, March 27, 1980.

Codman Research Group, Inc. *Final Report--Health Planning and Regulations: The New England Experience*. Washington, D.C.: U.S. Department of Health, Education and Welfare, September 30, 1979.

Colt, Avery M. "Elements of Comprehensive Health Planning." *American Journal of Public Health* 60(July 1970):1194-1204.

Consumer Commission on the Accreditation of Health Services, Inc. "Consumer Effectiveness: Now, and Under NHS." *Consumer Health Perspectives* 5(October 1978):1-4.

Crum, Gary. Personal Communication, Washington, D.C., June 1980.

99

100

Feinson, Clare. Testimony on behalf of the Consumer
Coalition for Health, before the Institute of
Medicine, Committee on Health Planning Goals and
Standards, March 27, 1980.

Fenerty, Anne. Statement on behalf of the Consumer
Coalition for Health, before the U.S. Congress, House
of Representatives, Committee on Interstate and Foreign
Commerce, Subcommittee on Health and the Environment,
H.R. 10460, Health Planning and Resources Development
Amendments of 1978, February 1, 1978.

Georgia Legal Services *et al.* Statement on behalf of
Legal Services Clients before the U.S. Congress, House
of Representatives, Committee on Interstate and Foreign
Commerce, Subcommittee on Health and the Environment,
H.R. 10460, Health Planning and Resources Development
Amendments of 1978, February 1, 1978.

Howell, Julianne. "Regulating Hospital Capital Investment: The Experience in Massachusetts." Ph.D.
dissertation, Harvard University, 1980. Mimeographed.

Iglehart, John K. "Executive-Congressional Coalition
Seeks Tighter Regulation for Medical-Services Industry." *National Journal* (November 10, 1973):1684-1692.

Institute of Medicine. *Controlling the Supply of Hospital
Beds.* Washington, D.C.: National Academy of Sciences,
1976.

Institute of Medicine. *Health Planning in the United
States: Issues in Guideline Development.* Washington,
D.C.: National Academy of Sciences, 1980.

Klarman, Herbert E. "Health Planning: Progress, Prospects
and Issues." *Milbank Memorial Fund Quarterly* 56
(1978): 78-112.

Klarman, Herbert E. "Observations on Health Care Tech-
nology: Measurement, Analysis, and Policy." In
*Medical Technology: The Culprit Behind Health Care
Costs?*, pp. 273-292. DHEW Publication No. PHS-79-3216.
Washington, D.C.: Government Printing Office. 1979.

Klarman, Herbert E. "National Policies and Local Planning
for Health Services." *Milbank Memorial Fund Quarterly*
54 (Winter 1976): 1-28.

Knox, Julian J. "The Functions of Consumers on Programs
and Policy Making of Health Systems Agencies and
Statewide Health Coordinating Councils." Memorandum
to the Chairman, National Council on Health Planning
and Development, May 5, 1978.

Koseki, Lawrence K., and Hayakawa, John M. "Consumer
Participation and Community Organization Practice.

Implications of National Health Legislation." *Medical Care* 17(March 1979):244-254.

Leach, Richard H. *American Federalism.* New York: W. W. Norton and Company, Inc., 1970.

Lipsky, Michael, and Lounds, Morris. "Citizen Participation and Health Care: Problems of Government Induced Participation." *Journal of Health Politics, Policy and Law* 1(Spring 1976):85-111.

Lowi, Theodore J. "American Business, Public Policy Case Studies and Political Theory." *World Politics* 16(1964): 677-715.

Marmor, Theodore R., and Morone, James. "HSA's and the Representation of Consumer Interests: Conceptual Issues and Litigation Problems." *Final Report.* Washington, D.C.: Government Printing Office, 1978.

McConnell, Grant. *Private Power and American Democracy.* New York: Knopf, 1967.

Merritt, Richard. Testimony on behalf of the National Conference of State Legislators, before the Institute of Medicine, Committee on Health Planning Goals and Standards, March 27, 1980.

Metsch, Jonathan M., and Veney, James E. "Consumer Participation and Social Accountability." *Medical Care* 14(April 1976):283-293.

Needleman, Jack, and Lewin, Lawrence S. "The Impact of State Regulation on the Adoption and Diffusion of New Medical Technology." In *Medical Technology and the Health Care System,* pp. 240-269. Washington, D.C.: National Academy of Sciences, 1979.

Paap, Warren R. "Consumer-Based Boards of Health Centers: Structural Problems in Achieving Effective Control." *American Journal of Public Health* 68(June 1978):578-582.

Raab, G. Gregory. "Intergovernmental Issues Raised by the National Health Planning Program." *Journal of Health and Human Resources Administration* 1(May 1979): 570-595.

Roberts, Marc. "The Political Economy of the Health System: What Can Planning Hope to Do." Presentation at the American Health Planning Association Annual Meeting, Boston, June 1, 1979.

Rosenbaum, Nelson M. "Evaluating Citizen Involvement Programs." In *Citizen Participation Perspectives, Proceedings of the National Conference on Citizen Participation, Washington, D.C., September 28 to October 1, 1978,* pp. 82-86. Edited by Stuart Langton. Medford: Lincoln Filene Center for Citizenship and Public Affairs, 1978.

Rosener, Judith B. "Citizen Participation: Can We Measure Its Effectiveness?" *Public Administration Review* (September/October 1978):457-463.

Rubel, Eugene. Personal Communication, Washington, D.C., March 1980.

Seidman, Harold. *Politics, Position and Power*. New York: Oxford University Press, 1980.

Shannon, Terry. "Report on Consumer Participation in the Health Planning Program." Paper prepared for the National Council on Health Planning and Development, Subcommittee on Implementation and Administration, June 1980.

Texas Association of Community Organizations for Reform Now (ACORN) v. Texas Area 5 Health Systems Agency, Inc., 77-1717 (5th Cir. 1977).

U.S. Congress, House, Committee on Interstate and Foreign Commerce. *National Health Policy, Planning and Resources Development Act of 1974*. H.R. Report 93-1382, 93rd Congress, 2nd Session, 1974.

Vladeck, Bruce C. "Health Planning--Participation and Its Discontents." *American Journal of Public Health* 69(April 1979):331-332.

Vladeck, Bruce C. "Interest-Group Representation and the HSAs: Health Planning and Political Theory." *American Journal of Public Health* 67(January 1977):23-28.

Vladeck, Bruce C. "The Market vs. Regulation: The Case for Regulation." Paper prepared for the Project Hope Symposium on Health Care Regulation and Competition: Are They Compatible? Millwood, Virginia, May 22-25, 1980.

BIBLIOGRAPHY

Advisory Commission on Intergovernmental Relations.
    *The Intergovernmental Grant System as Seen by Local,
    State and Federal Officials*. Washington, D.C.:
    Government Printing Office, March 1977.
Altman, Drew. "The Politics of Health Care Regulation:
    The Case of the National Health Planning and Resources
    Development Act." *Journal of Health Politics, Policy
    and Law* 2(Winter 1978):560-580.
Altman, Drew, and Sapolsky, Harvey M. "Writing the
    Regulations for Health." *Policy Sciences* 7(December
    1976):417-437.
Altman, Stuart H., and Weiner, Sanford L. "Constraining
    the Medical Care System: Regulation as a Second Best
    Strategy." Paper prepared for the Federal Trade
    Commission Conference on Competition in the Health
    Care Sector: Past, Present and Future, Washington,
    D.C., June 1977. Typewritten.
American Health Planning Association. "Final Report on
    1978 Survey of Health Planning Agencies." January
    1979. Typewritten.
American Hospital Association, Department of Health
    Planning. "Certificate of Need, Annual Survey 1978."
    Typewritten.
American Medical Association. Statement Before the United
    States Senate, Committee on Human Resources, Subcom-
    mittee on Health and Scientific Research, S. 2410, The
    Health Planning Amendments of 1978, February 3, 1978.
Aron, Joan B. "Citizen Participation at Government
    Expense." *Public Administration Review* 5(September/
    October 1979):447-485.
Austin, David M. "Resident Participation: Political
    Mobilization or Organizational Co-optation?" *Public
    Administration Review* 32(1972):409-420.

Bellin, Seymour S.; Geiger, H. Jack; and Gibson, Count. "Impact of Ambulatory Health-Care Services on the Demand for Hospital Beds." *New England Journal of Medicine* 280(April 10, 1969):808-812.

Bernstein, Marver. *Regulating Business by Independent Commission*. Princeton: Princeton University Press, 1955.

Berry, David E. "The National Health Planning and Resources Development Act: An Academic Perspective." *State and Local Government Review* 12(May 1980):69-73.

Bice, Thomas W. "Health Planning and Regulation Effects on Hospital Costs." In *Annual Review of Public Health,* pp. 137-161. Edited by L. Breslow, J. E. Fielding, and L. B. Lave. Palo Alto: Annual Reviews, Inc., 1980.

Bice, Thomas W., and Eichhorn, R. L. "Evaluation of Public Health Programs." In *Handbook of Evaluation Research*, Vol. II, pp. 605-620. Edited by M. Guttentag and E. L. Struening. Beverly Hills: Sage Publications, 1975.

Bicknell, William J., and Walsh, Diana C. "Critical Experiences in Organizing and Administering a State Certificate of Need Program." *Public Health Reports* 91(January-February 1976):29-45.

Bjorman, James W., and Altenstetter, Christa. "Accountability in Health Care: An Essay on Mechanisms, Muddles, and Mires." *Journal of Health Politics, Policy and Law* 4(Fall 1979):360-381.

Blum, Henrik L. *Planning for Health*. New York: Human Sciences Press, 1974, pp. 487-494, 513-517.

Bogue, Ted. Statement on Behalf of the Public Citizen Health Research Group, before the National Council on Health Planning and Development, Subcommittee on Implementation and Administration, Consumer Involvement in Health Planning, May 10, 1979.

Bolan, Richard S. "Community Decision Behavior: The Culture of Planning." *American Institute of Planners Journal* (September 1969):301-310.

Bosch, Samuel J.; Merino, Rolando; and Zambrana, Ruth. "Training of a Community Board to Increase the Effectiveness of a Health Center." *Public Health Reports* 94(May-June 1979):275-280.

Brieland, Donald. "Community Advisory Boards and Maximum Feasible Participation." *American Journal of Public Health* 61(February 1971): 292-296.

Bromberg, Michael D. "Health Planning and Certificate of

Need: Can Protectionism be Justified?" Paper prepared for the Project Hope Symposium on Regulation
and Competition: Are They Compatible?, Millwood,
Virginia, May 22-25, 1980.

Brown, Lawrence D., and Frieden, Bernard J. "Rulemaking
by Improvisation: Guidelines and Goals in the Model
Cities Program." *Policy Sciences* 7(December 1976):
455-488.

Bulgaro, Patrick J., and Webb, Arthur Y. "Federal-State
Conflicts in Cost Control." *Proceedings of the
Academy of Political Science* 33(1980):92-110.

Buntz, C. Gregory; Macaluso, Theodore F.; and Azarow,
Jay Allan. "Federal Influence on State Health Policy."
Journal of Health Politics, Policy and Law 3(Spring
1978):71-86.

Califano, Joseph A., Jr. Remarks Before the Institute
of Medicine, National Academy of Sciences, Washington,
D.C., October 26, 1978.

California Public Interest Research Group. "Diary of a
Health Training Group." *Calpirg Reports* 7(October
1979):1-3.

Checkoway, Barry. "Citizens on Local Health Planning
Boards: What Are The Obstacles?" *Journal of the
Community Development Society* 10(Fall 1979):101-116.

Checkoway, Barry. "Consumer Issues Around HSAs: The
Case of the Champaign County Health Care Consumers."
Health Law Project Library Bulletin 3(March 1977):
23-25.

Checkoway, Barry. "Making Consumer Participation Work
under PL 93-641: A Proposal to the National Council
on Health Planning and Development." Urbana, Illinois:
Department of Regional Planning, University of Illinois
at Urbana, Champaign, March 7, 1979. Typewritten.

Checkoway, Barry. "Rx for Health Care Agencies: Doses of
Consumer Help." *Planning* 32(November 1977):16-17.

Checkoway, Barry; O'Rourke, Thomas; and Macrina, David.
"Who Do Providers Represent?" *Health Law Project
Library Bulletin* 5(February 1980):49-53.

Checkoway, Barry. Statement before the U.S. Congress,
House of Representatives, Subcommittee on Health and
the Environment, Public Involvement in Local Health
Care Planning, February 1, 1978.

Checkoway, Barry, and Van Til, J. "What Do We Know About
Citizen Participation?" In *Citizen Participation in
America*. Edited by Stuart Langton. Lexington:
D. C. Heath, 1978.

Chesney, James D. "Problems of Representation in Health Systems Agencies." Ann Arbor: Department of Health Planning and Administration, University of Michigan School of Public Health, September 1978. Typewritten.

Clark, Noreen M., and Pinkett-Heller, Marcia. "Developing HSA Leadership: An Innovation in Board Education." *American Journal of Health Planning* 2(July 1977):9-13.

Clark, Robert F. "Evaluating Citizen Participation in Community Services Programs: Elements of a Strategy." Paper prepared for the Symposium on Citizen Participation, Models and Methods of Evaluation, Washington, D.C., February 4, 1980.

Clarke, Gary J. "The Role of the States in the Delivery of Health Services." Washington, D.C.: Intergovernmental Health Policy Project, George Washington University, October 1979. Typewritten.

Cohen, Harold A. "Rate Setting and Competition: Are They Compatible?" Paper prepared for the Project Hope Symposium on Health Care Regulation and Competition: Are They Compatible?, Millwood, Virginia, May 22-25, 1980.

Consumer Commission on the Accreditation of Health Services, Inc. "Freedom of Information, The Right of the Public to Know." *Health Perspectives* 1(July-August 1974):1-6.

Consumer Commission on the Accreditation of Health Services, Inc. "Full and Equal Participation, A Consumer Objective." *Health Perspectives* 3(May-June 1976):1-5.

Consumer Commission on the Accreditation of Health Services, Inc. "Health Planning: A Consumer View." *Health Perspectives* 3(March-April 1976):1-8.

Consumer Commission on the Accreditation of Health Services, Inc. "Health Planning and Reimbursement." *Health Perspectives* 3(July-August 1976):1-6.

Consumer Commission on the Accreditation of Health Services, Inc. "The Development of a Consumer Health Network." *Health Perspectives* 4(July-October 1977): 1-12.

Consumer Health Action Network. "Budget Cuts Proposals Threaten Planning Project." *Consumer Health Action Network (CHAN)* 5(May/June 1980):1-3.

Consumer Health Action Network. "No Antitrust Clearance for Some Planning Activities." *Consumer Health Action Network (CHAN)* 5(May/June 1980):2.

Consumer Health Action Network. "P-R-O-V-I-D-E-R Spells
    Consumer." *Consumer Health Action Network (CHAN)*
    5(May/June 1980):3-4.

Coombs, Jeanne A.; Skinner, Mathew J.; and Walsh, Diana
    Chapman. "A Systematic Approach to Community Educa-
    tion." *American Journal of Health Planning* 2(July
    1977): 14-18.

Cooper, Terry L. "The Hidden Price Tag: Participation
    Costs and Health Planning." *American Journal of
    Public Health* 69(April 1979):368-374.

Curran, William J. "The Health Planners and Computerized
    Tomography: High Technology, Cost Control, and Judi-
    cial Review." *New England Journal of Medicine* 303
    (September 11, 1980):626-627.

Curran, William J. "The Confrontation Between National
    Health Planning and the Federal Anti-Trust Laws."
    American Journal of Public Health 70(April 1980):425-
    426.

Dahl, Robert A., and Lindblom, Charles E. *Politics,
    Economics, and Welfare*. Chicago: University of
    Chicago Press, 1976.

Danaceau, Paul. *Consumer Participation In Health Care:
    How It's Working*. Arlington: Human Services Insti-
    tute for Children and Families, Inc., 1975.

Daniels, Robert S. "Governance and Administration of
    Human Services in Urban Low-Income Communities."
    American Journal of Public Health 63(August 1973):
    715-720.

Davis, James W. "Decentralization, Citizen Participa-
    tion, and Ghetto Health Care." *American Behavioral
    Scientist* 15(September/October 1971):94-107.

Dawson, Richard E., and Gray, Virginia. "State Welfare
    Policies." In *Politics in the American States,* 2nd
    edition, pp. 433-46. Edited by Herbert Jacob and
    Kenneth N. Vine. Boston: Little, Brown and Company,
    1971.

Demkovich, Linda E. "Cutting Health Care Costs--Why
    Not Let the Market Decide?" *National Journal*
    (October 27, 1979):1796-1800.

Demkovich, Linda E. "Scaring the Planners." *National
    Journal* (May 31, 1980):905.

Derthick, Martha. "Guidelines for Social Services Grants."
    Policy Sciences 7(1976):489-504.

DeVries, Robert A. "CEO Don Educator's Cap." *Hospitals*
    (January 16, 1980):108-111.

Dorwart, Robert A.; Meyers, William R.; and Norman, Edward
C. "Effective Citizen Participation in Mental Health:
Comparative Case Studies." *Public Health Reports*
94(May-June 1979):268-274.

Douglass, Chester W. "Representation Patterns in Community Health Decision Making." *Journal of Health
and Social Behavior* 14(1973):80.

Douglass, Chester W. "Consumer Influence in Health
Planning in the Urban Ghetto." *Inquiry* 12(June 1975):
157-163.

Downs, Anthony. *Inside Bureaucracy*. Boston: Little,
Brown and Company, 1967.

Dye, Thomas R. *Policy Analysis: What Governments Do,
Why They Do It, and What Difference It Makes*. University, Alabama: University of Alabama Press, 1976.

Ellenburg, Dorothy. "Consumer Agendas and Health Planning
Priorities: One Consumer's Perspective." *State and
Local Government Review* 12(May 1980):61-68.

Ellenburg, Dorothy. "Site Visits: Under-Represented
Community Interests: An Assessment of Involvement of
Community Groups, Organizations and Agencies in Local
Health Planning Activities." A Report to the Subcommittee on National Guidelines, Goals, Standards,
and Priorities. Washington, D.C.: National Council
on Health Planning and Development, November 7, 1979.

Ellenburg, Dorothy. Statement Before the National Council on Health Planning and Development, Subcommittee
on Implementation and Administration, Consumer Participation, May 10, 1979.

Ellwood, Paul M., Jr.; McClure, Walter J.; and Rosala,
John C. *How Business Interacts with the Health Care
System*. Washington, D.C.: National Chamber of Com-
merce Foundation, 1978.

Ensminger, Barry. "Health Advocacy in Search of an
Office." *Consumer Health Perspectives* 5(October 1978):
5-6.

Enthoven, Alain, and Noll, Richard. "Regulatory and
Nonregulatory Strategies for Controlling Health Care
Costs." Paper prepared for the Sun Valley Forum,
August 1977.

Ewing, Margaret F. "Health Planning and Deinstitutional-
ization: Advocacy within the Administrative Process."
Stanford Law Review 31 (April 1979):355-365.

Fearon, Zita. "Consumer Participation: Sinking or
Swimming?" *Consumer Health Perspectives* 6(February
1980):2-6.

109

Feder, Judith, and Holahan, John. "Administrative Choices."
    In *National Health Insurance: Conflicting Goals and
    Policy Choices,* pp. 21-72. Edited by Judith Feder,
    John Holahan, and Theodore Marmor. Washington, D.C.:
    The Urban Institute, 1980.
Federal Register. "Part II--Department of Health, Educa-
    tion and Welfare, Health Resources Administration,
    Governing Body Requirements for Health Systems Agencies,
    Notice of Proposed Rulemaking." Friday, May 26, 1978,
    22858-22861.
Federal Register. "Part II--Draft Consumer Programs."
    Monday, February 4, 1980, 7696-7747.
Federal Register. Part II--Section A, Consumer Affairs
    Council." Monday, February 4, 1980, 7697-7735.
Federal Register. Part VIII--Department of Health, Educa-
    tion and Welfare, Public Health Service, Medical
    Facilities Construction and Modernization; Require-
    ments for Provision of Services to Persons Unable to
    Pay and Community Service by Assisted Health Facili-
    ties." Friday, May 18, 1979, 29372-29410.
Feingold, Eugene. "A Political Scientist's View of the
    Neighborhood Health Center as a New Social Institu-
    tion." *Medical Care* 8(March-April 1970):108-115.
Feshbach, Dan. "What's Inside the Black Box: A Case
    Study of Allocative Politics in the Hill-Burton Pro-
    gram." *International Journal of Health Services*
    9(1979):313-339.
Field, Marilyn J., and Koontz, Virginia L. "Evaluating
    Health Systems Agency Performance." *Journal of
    Health and Human Resources Administration* (May 1980):
    471-490.
Finney, Robert D., and Newman, Charles A. "Health Sys-
    tems Agencies, A Civil Rights Forum." *Urban Health*
    8(July-August 1979):18-20, 44.
Fiori, Florence B. "Bureau of Health Facilities' In-
    creasing Responsibilities in Assuring Medical Care
    for the Needy and Services Without Discrimination."
    Public Health Reports 95(March-April 1980):164-173.
Frost, S. B.; Fearon, Zita; and Hyman, Herbert H. *A
    Consumer's Guide to Evaluating Medical Technology.*
    Consumer Commission on the Accreditation of Health
    Services, Inc., 1979.
Fullarton, Jane E. "The Evaluation of Citizen Participa-
    tion in Health Programs." Paper prepared for the
    Symposium on Citizen Participation, Models and Methods
    of Evaluation, Washington, D.C., February 4, 1980.

Fulton, Bill. "Should Regulators Pay the Public to Take Part in Their Proceedings?" *National Journal* (May 10, 1980):776-778.

Glenn, Karen, and Lipschultz, Claire. *Tools for Health Planning: A Consumer Workbook.* San Diego: California Public Interest Research Group, 1979.

Goldberg, George A.; Trowbridge, Frederick L.; and Buxbaum, Robert C. "Issues in the Development of Neighborhood Health Centers." *Inquiry* 6(March 1969):37-47.

Goldberg, Mark. "The Context for Evaluation." Paper prepared for the Symposium on Citizen Participation, Models and Methods of Evaluation, Washington, D.C., February 4, 1980.

Graves, W. Brooke. *American Intergovernmental Relations: Their Origins, Historical Development and Current Status.* New York: Scribner's Sons, 1964.

Gray, Virginia. "Innovation in the States: A Diffusion Study." *American Political Science Review* 67(December 1973):1174-1185.

Greer, Ann Lennarson. "Training Board Members for Health Planning Agencies." *Public Health Reports* 91(January-February 1976):56-61.

Greer, Scott, and Greer, Ann Lennarson. "Governance By Citizens' Boards: The Case of Community Mental Health Centers." In *The Practice of Policy Evaluation Research.* Edited by David Nachmias. New York: St. Martin's Press, 1979.

Grodzins, Morton. *The American System: A New View of Government in the United States.* Edited by Daniel J. Elazar. Chicago: Rand McNally, 1966.

Grossman, Randolph M. "Voting Behavior of HSA Interest Groups: A Case Study." *American Journal of Public Health* 68(December 1978):1191-1194.

Grum, J. G. "The Effects of Legislative Structure on Legislative Performance." In *State and Urban Politics,* pp. 298-322. Edited by Richard I. Hofferbert and Ira Sharkansky. Boston: Little, Brown and Company, 1971.

Haider, Donald. *When Governments Come to Washington: Governors, Mayors, and Intergovernmental Lobbying.* New York: The Free Press, 1974.

Harris, L., and Associates. *Hospital Care in America.* Nashville: Hospital Affiliates International, 1978.

Harvey, E., and Mills, R. "Patterns of Organizational Adaptation: A Political Perspective." In *Power in Organizations,* pp. 181-213. Edited by M. N. Zald. Nashville: Vanderbilt University Press, 1970.

Havighurst, Clark C. "Competition in Health Services--
An Equal Number of Questions and Answers." Paper pre-
pared for the Project Hope Symposium on Competition and
Regulation: Are They Compatible?, Millwood, Virginia,
May 22-25, 1980.

Haynes, M. A. "Professionals in the Community Confront
Change." *American Journal of Public Health* 60(March
1970):519-523.

Hersch, Charles. "Social History, Mental Health, and
Community Control." *American Psychologist* 27(August
1972):749-754.

Hochbaum, G. M. "Consumer Participation in Health Planning: Toward Conceptual Clarification." *American
Journal of Public Health* 59(September 1969):1698-1705.

Holton, Wilfred E.; New, Peter K.; and Hessler, R. M.
"Citizen Participation and Conflict." *Administration of
Mental Health* 96(Fall 1973).

Howard, L. K. "Decentralization and Citizen Participation
in Health Services." *Public Administration Review*
32(1972):701.

Howell, Julianne R. "The Impact of Capital Expenditure
Regulation on Hospitals: A Review of Current Evidence."
Cambridge, Massachusetts: Public Policy Program,
Kennedy School of Government, Harvard University.
January 20, 1977. Mimeographed.

Hughes, Edward. "Technological Innovation Under Regulatory
and Competitive Cost Containment." Paper prepared for
the Project Hope Symposium on Competition and Regulation: Are They Compatible?, Millwood, Virginia, May
22-25, 1980.

Iglehart, John K. "Congress Expands Capacity to Contest
Executive Policy." *National Journal* (May 17, 1975):
730-739.

Iglehart, John K. "Health Planning Program Struggles to
Make a Case for Itself." *National Journal* (November
13, 1976):1632-1638.

Iglehart, John K. "HEW Moves to Implement New Planning-
Regulation Program." *National Journal* (January 25,
1975):147.

Iglehart, John K. "HEW Takes Final Step Down Road to
Local Health Planning Network." *National Journal*
(April 3, 1976):436-439.

Iglehart, John K. "It's Back to the Drawing Board for the
Health Planning Act." *National Journal* (December 31,
1977):1996-2000.

Iglehart, John K. "States, Cities Seek Role Over Regional
Policy Bodies." *National Journal* (August 23, 1975):1207.

112

Jacobson, Solomon G. "Approaches to the Evaluation of Citizen Participation in Human Services Decisionmaking, Planning and Delivery." Paper prepared for the Symposium on Citizen Participation, Models and Methods of Evaluation, Washington, D.C., February 4, 1980.

Jonas, Steven. "A Theoretical Approach to the Question of 'Community Control' of Health Services Facilities." *American Journal of Public Health* 61(May 1971):916-921.

Jonas, Steven. Editorial. "Limitations of Community Control of Health Facilities and Services." *American Journal of Public Health* 68(June 1978):541-543.

Kane, Daniel A. "Community Participation in the Health Services System." *Hospital Administration* 16(Winter 1971):36-43.

Kerr, Frederick H. "Coping with your HSA." *Hospital and Health Services Administration* (Summer 1980):5-15.

Kimmey, James R. "The Congress and Competition in the Health Industry." Paper prepared for the Project Hope Symposium on Competition and Regulation: Are They Compatible?, Millwood, Virginia, May 22-25, 1980.

Kinzer, David M. "A Provider Perspective on P.L. 93-641." *State and Local Government Review* 12(May 1980):52-61.

Kissam, Philip C. "The Third Mode and Its Nemesis: Professional Self-Regulation by Physicians and Conflicts of Interest." Paper prepared for the Project Hope Symposium on Health Care Regulation and Competition: Are They Compatible?, Millwood, Virginia, May 22-25, 1980.

Klarman, Herbert E. "Data Collection and Application for Health Planning." Paper prepared for seminar sponsored by the National Center for Health Statistics and the Bureau of Health Planning and Development, Rockville, Maryland, January 11, 1977.

Klarman, Herbert E. "Observations on Health Services Research and Health Policy Analysis." *Milbank Memorial Fund Quarterly* 58(Spring 1980):201-216.

Klein, Rudolf. "Control, Participation, and the British National Health Service." *Milbank Memorial Fund Quarterly* 57(1979):70-94.

Klein, Rudolf. "Evidence to the Royal Commission on the National Health Service." *Journal of Health Politics, Policy and Law* 3(Spring 1978):11-19.

Krowka, Michael J., and Peck, Owen C. "Relating Health Planning Concepts to Medical Students." *Journal of Medical Education* 54(December 1979):946-947.

Levin, Arthur. "Consumer Participation: Futile Efforts

in a Misguided System." *Consumer Health Perspectives* 6(February 1980):6-8.

Lewin and Associates, Inc. "Evaluation of the Efficiency and Effectiveness of the Section 1122 Review Process." Springfield, Virginia: National Technical Information Service, 1976.

Lewis, Thomas J. "Community Participation in the Certificate-of-Need Process: A Look at Ten-Taxpayer Groups in Massachusetts." *American Journal of Law and Medicine* 5(Fall 1979):215-230.

Lindblom, Charles E. *The Intelligence of Democracy.* New York: The Free Press, 1965.

Lowe, Linda. Statement on Behalf of the Georgia Legal Services Before the National Council on Health Planning and Development, Subcommittee on Implementation and Administration, Consumer Involvement in Health Planning, May 10, 1979.

Luft, Harold S., and Frisvold, Gary A. "Decisionmaking in Regional Planning Agencies." *Journal of Health Politics, Policy and Law* 4(Summer 1979):250-272.

Marmor, Theodore R. "Consumer Representation: Beneath the Consensus, Many Difficulties." *Trustee* 30(April 1977):37-40.

Marmor, Theodore R., and Morone, James A. "Health Care Regulatory Policy Requires Centralized Authority." *Hospitals* 50(March 1, 1976):83-88.

Marmor, Theodore R.; Wittman, Donald; and Heagy, Thomas. "The Politics of Medical Inflation." *Journal of Health Politics, Policy and Law* 1(Spring 1976):69-84.

Meier, Gerald B., and Hunter, Mary M. *How Business Can Stimulate a Competitive Health Care System.* Washington, D.C.: National Chamber of Commerce Foundation, 1978.

Mikulecky, Thomas J. "Intergovernmental Relations Strategies for the Local Manager." *Public Administration Review* 4(July/August 1980):379-381.

Miller, C. Hope, and Schoeman, Milton. "Program Information Note--HSA Governing Body Officials." U.S. Department of Health and Human Services, Health Resources Administration, Bureau of Health Planning, Office of Program Development, September 2, 1980.

Mock, Ron. "Intergovernmental Power and Dependence." *Public Administration Review* 39, No. 6(November/December 1979): 556-561.

Montgomery, Dean. "The Community as Laboratory. A View of Health Systems Planning from a Local Perspective." *State and Local Government Review* 12(May 1980):50-56.

Morone, James A. "The Ambiguous Success of Citizen Participation: Politics, Planning and Health Care." Paper prepared for the American Political Science Convention, Washington, D.C., August 1980.

Morone, James A., and Marmor, Theodore R. "Representing Consumer Interests: The Case of American Health Planning." *American Journal of Community Psychology* 8(1980):19-30.

Mott, Basil J. F. Editorial. "Health Systems Agencies: Politics of Project Review." *American Journal of Public Health* 68(December 1978):1173-1174.

Murrell, Stanley A., and Schulte, Paul. "A Procedure for Systematic Citizen Input to Community Decision-Making." *American Journal of Community Psychology* 8(1980):19-30.

National Governors' Association, Center for Policy Research. "The State Perspective: The Report of the Health Policy Consortium Phase 3." June 1979.

National Governors' Conference, Center for Policy Research and Analysis. "Making the National Health Planning Law Work: The State Perspective." February 1977.

Needleman, Jack, and Lewin & Associates, Inc. "Promoting Competition as a Regulatory Strategy." Paper prepared for the Alpha Center for Health Planning, June 1980.

New, Peter K.; Hessler, R. M.; and Carter, P. B. "Consumer Control and Public Accountability." *The Anthropological Quarterly* 46(July 1973): 196-213.

Nutt, Paul C. "Some Considerations in Selecting Interactive and Analytical Decision Approaches for EMS Councils." *Medical Care* 17(February 1979):152-167.

Onibokun, Adepoju G., and Curry, Martha. "An Ideology of Citizen Participation: The Metropolitan Seattle Transit Case Study." *Public Administration Review* 36, No. 6,(May/June 1976):269-277.

Orkand Corporation. *Assessment of Representation and Parity for HSAs and SHPDAs*. Rockville: Orkand Corporation, March 1977.

Parker, Alberta W. "The Consumer as Policy-Maker--Issues of Training." *American Journal of Public Health* 60 (November 1970):2139-2153.

Parkum, Kurt H., and Parkum, Virginia C. *Voluntary Participation in Health Planning: A Study of Health Consumer and Provider Participation in Selected Areas of Pennsylvania*. Harrisburg: Pennsylvania Department of Health, 1973.

115

Partridge, Kay B. "Community and Professional Participation in Decision-Making at a Health Center." *Health Services Reports* 88(June-July 1973):527-534.

Pastreich, B. "A Report on Health Care Organization in Massachusetts: Union and Community Unite Around Health Care." *Health Law Project Library Bulletin* 331(April 1977):1-4.

Pauly, Mark V. "Certificate of Need and Market Efficiency." Paper prepared for the Project Hope Symposium on Health Care Regulation and Competition: Are They Compatible?, Millwood, Virginia, May 22-25, 1980.

Peirce, Neal R. "Proposed Reforms Spark Civil Service Debate." *National Journal* 7(November 29, 1975):1643-1648.

Phillips, Harry T. Editorial. "A House Divided." *American Journal of Public Health* 66(August 1976): 737-738.

Pitkin, Hanna F. *The Concept of Representation*. Berkeley: University of California Press, 1972.

Raab, G. Gregory. "Intergovernmental Issues Raised by the National Health Planning Program." *Journal of Health and Human Resources Administration* 1(May 1979): 570-595.

Raab, G. Gregory. "Health Planning and American Federalism." Ph.D. dissertation, University of Virginia, Charlottesville, Virginia, May 1980.

Rabinovitz, Francine; Pressman, Jeffrey; and Rein, Martha. "Guidelines: A Plethora of Forms, Authors, and Functions." *Policy Sciences* 7(December 1976): 399-416.

Ready, W. E. "The Consumer's Role in the Politics of Health Planning." *Health Education Monographs* 32(1972).

Reagan, Michael. *The New Federalism*. New York: Oxford University Press, 1972.

Resnick, Lindsay R. "Issue Paper: Federal, State and Local Relationships in Health Planning." Paper prepared for the National Council on Health Planning and Development, Subcommittee on Implementation and Administration, May 19, 1980.

Riska, E., and Taylor, J. A. "Consumer Attitudes Toward Health Policy and Knowledge About Health Legislation." *Journal of Health Politics, Policy and Law* 3(Spring 1978):112-123.

Rocheleau, Bruce. "How Do We Measure the Impact of Intergovernmental Programs? Some Problems and Examples from the Health Area." *Journal of Health Politics, Policy and Law* 4(Winter 1980):605-618.

Rocheleau, Bruce, and Warren, Steven. "Health Planners and Local Public Finance--the Case for Revenue Sharing." *Public Health Reports* 95(July-August 1980):313-320.

Rogatz, Peter. "Medical Technology and the Health Care Consumer: An Overview." *Consumer Health Perspectives* 5(November 1978):1-2.

Rorrie, Colin C., Jr. Memorandum. "Broadly Representative Governing Bodies: Determining Compliance with P.L. 93-641." Bureau of Health Planning, Department of Health and Human Services, Hyattsville, Maryland, January 3, 1979.

Rorrie, Colin C., Jr. and Dearman, Frances V. "Health Planning--A New Phase." *Public Health Reports* 95 (March/April 1980):177-182.

Rorrie, Colin C., Jr. and Shannon, Terry E. "Health Planning: Experience and Expectations." *State and Local Government Review* 12(May 1980):45-50.

Rose, Douglas D. "National and Local Forces in State Politics: The Implications of Multi-Level Policy Analysis." *The American Political Science Review* 67(December 1973):1162-1173.

Rose, Marilyn G. "Federal Regulation of Services to the Poor Under the Hill-Burton Act: Realities and Pitfalls." *Northwestern University Law Review* 70(1975): 168-201.

Rosenbaum, Nelson M. "Citizen Participation and Democratic Theory." In *Citizen Participation in America,* pp. 43-54. Edited by Stuart Langton. Lexington: Lexington Books, 1978.

Rosenbaum, Nelson M. "The Origins of Citizen Involvement in Federal Programs." In *Anticipatory Democracy, People in the Politics of the Future,* pp. 139-154. Edited by Clement Bezold. New York: Vintage Books, 1978.

Salber, Eva J. "Consumer Participation in Neighborhood Health Centers." *New England Journal of Medicine* 283(September 3, 1970):515-518.

Salkever, David S. "Competition Among Hospitals." Paper prepared for Federal Trade Commission Conference on Competition in the Health Care Sector: Past, Present and Future, Washington, D.C., June 1-2, 1977.

Sanford, Terry. *Storm Over the States.* New York: McGraw Hill, 1967.

Savas, E. S., and Ginsburg, Sigmund G. "The Civil Service: A Meritless System?" *The Public Interest* 32(Summer 1973):70-85.

117

Schwab, Paul M. "A Symposium--State and Local Govern-
mental Aspects of Health Care, An Overview." *State
and Local Government Review* 12(May 1980):42-44.
Semmel, Herbert. Statement on Behalf of the Consumer
Coalition for Health, before the U.S. Congress, House
of Representatives, Committee on Interstate and Foreign
Commerce, Subcommittee on Health and the Environment,
H.R. 10460, Health Planning and Resources Development
Amendments of 1978, February 1, 1978.
Sharkansky, Ira, and Hofferbert, Richard I. "Dimensions
of State Politics, Economics and Public Policy." *The
American Political Science Review* 63(September 1969):
867-869.
Sigmond, Robert M. "Health Planning." *Medical Care*
5(May-June 1967):117-128.
Sigmond, Robert M. "Hospital Planning in Allegheny
County." Paper presented at the National Health Forum,
Planning for Health, Chicago, Illinois, March 22, 1967.
Sigmond, Robert M. "The Hospital Planning Process and
the Community." In *Areawide Planning*. Chicago:
American Medical Association, 1965.
Sigmond, Robert M. "The Linkage Between Health Policy-
Making and Planning." Paper presented to the Annual
Health Conference of the New York Academy of Medicine,
April 28, 1977.
Simson, S. P., and Bleiweiss, L. J. "Transforming the
Orientation of a Health Organization Through Community
Involvement." *Journal of Sociology and Social Welfare*
2(1974):198-206.
Sparer, Gerald; Dines, G. R.; and Smith, D. "Consumer
Participation in OEO-Assisted Neighborhood Health
Centers." *American Journal of Public Health* 60(June
1970):1091-1102.
Stanfield, Rochelle L. "Federal Aid Comes Out of the
Closet in the Mountain and Desert West." *National
Journal* (December 15, 1979):2096-2099.
Statement of Senator Edward M. Kennedy, Chairman of the
Senate Health and Scientific Research Subcommittee,
at a Hearing on the Urban Health Crisis and the Need
for Improved Health Planning at the Martin Luther
King, Jr., Hospital, November 12, 1977.
Steckler, Allan, and Dawson, Leonard. "Determinants of
Consumer Influence in a Health Systems Agency."
Health Education Monographs 6(Winter 1978):378-393.

Steckler, Allan B., and Herzog, William T. "How to Keep Your Mandated Citizen Board Out of Your Hair and Off of Your Back: A Guide for Executive Directors." *American Journal of Public Health* 69(August 1979):809-812.

Steckler, George, Jr. "Certificate of Need--A Systems Analysis of Maryland's Experience and Plans." *American Journal of Public Health* 63(November 1973):966-972.

Strauss, Marvin D.; Harten, Carol J.; and Kempner, Mark A. "Training of Planning Personnel for Local and State Agencies." *Public Health Reports* 91(January-February 1976):51-55.

Sundquist, James, with the collaboration of Davis, David W. *Making Federalism Work.* Washington, D.C.: The Brookings Institution, 1969.

Sypniewski, B. P., and Semmel, H. "From Little Acorns . . . Representation on Health Systems Agencies." *Health Law Project Library Bulletin* 335(September 1977):1-6.

Technical Assistance Research Programs, Inc. "An Assessment of HSA Board Selection and Operating Procedures." Report prepared for U.S. Department of Health, Education and Welfare, Contract No. HRA-232-78-0165.

Terrell, Paul. "Beyond the Categories: Human Service Managers View the New Federal Aid." *Public Administration Review* 40, No. 1(January-February 1980):47-54.

The Urban Institute. "National Health Insurance: Policy Choices for the 1980's." *Policy and Research Report* 9(Winter 1979):1-8.

The White House Press Office, Office of Media Liaison. "Health Planning--the 1981 Budget." Background paper, June 17, 1980.

Thompson, R. "The Whys and Why Nots of Consumer Participation." *Community Mental Health Journal* 9(1973):143-150.

Tillotson, John K., and Rosala, John C. *How Business Can Use Specific Techniques to Control Health Care Costs.* Washington, D.C.: National Chamber of Commerce Foundation, 1978.

Tischler, Gary L. "The Effects of Consumer Control on the Delivery of Services." *American Journal of Orthopsychiatry* 41(April 1971):501-505.

U.S. Congress, House, Committee on Interstate and Foreign Commerce. *Health Planning and Resources Development Amendments of 1978.* H.R. Report 95-1185, 95th Congress 2nd Session, 1978.

U.S. Congress, House, Committee on Interstate and Foreign Commerce. *Health Planning and Resources Development*

Amendments of 1979. H.R. Report 96-190, 96th Congress
1st Session, 1979.

U.S. Congress, House, Committee on Interstate and Foreign
Commerce. *National Health Planning Guidelines.* Hear-
ing before Subcommittee on Health and the Environment,
H.R. 95-53, 95th Congress 1st Session, 1977.

U.S. Congress, House, Committee on Interstate and Foreign
Commerce, Subcommittee on Health and the Environment.
Hearings on H.R. 10460. Washington, D.C.: Government
Printing Office, 1978.

U.S. Congress, House. *Health Planning and Resources
Development Act of 1974.* House Conference Report 93-
1640, 93rd Congress 2nd Session, 1974.

U.S. Congress, House. *Health Planning and Resources
Development Amendments of 1979.* House Conference Report 96-420, 96th Congress 1st Session, 1979.

U.S. Congress, Senate, Committee on Human Resources.
Health Planning Amendments of 1978. S. Report 95-845,
95th Congress 2nd Session, 1978.

U.S. Congress, Senate, Committee on Labor and Human
Resources. *Health Planning Amendments of 1979.*
S. Report 96-96, 96th Congress 1st Session, 1979.

U.S. Congress, Senate. *Health Planning and Resources
Development Amendments of 1979.* P.L. 96-79, 96th
Congress 1st Session, 1979, S.544.

U.S. Congress, Senate. *National Health Planning and
Resources Development Act of 1974.* P.L. 93-641,
93rd Congress 2nd Session, 1975, S. 2994.

U.S. Department of Commerce, Bureau of the Census.
"Estimates of the Population of the United States, by
Age, Race, and Sex: 1976 to 1979." *Current Popula-
tion Reports,* Series P-25, No. 870, January 1980.

U.S. Department of Commerce, Bureau of the Census.
"Language Usage in the United States: July 1975."
Current Population Reports, Series P-23, No. 60, July
1976.

U.S. Department of Commerce, Bureau of the Census. "Money
Income of Families and Persons in the United States:
1978." *Current Population Reports,* Series P-60, No.
123, June 1980.

U.S. Department of Health and Human Services, Health
Services Administration, Public Health Service. "States
Urged to Use Section 1122 Review." *Health Resources
News* 7(June 1980):1-3.

U.S. Department of Health and Human Services, Public
Health Service. "Summary of the 1979 Health Planning

Amendments." *Public Health Reports* 95(March-April 1980):183-188.

U.S. Department of Health, Education and Welfare. *Educating The Public About Health: A Planning Guide.* Washington, D.C.: Government Printing Office, 1977.

U.S. Department of Health, Education and Welfare, Health Resources Administration, Bureau of Health Planning and Resources Development, Office of Operations Monitoring. "Health Systems Agency Performance Standards Guidelines." February 1, 1977. Typewritten.

U.S. Department of Health, Education and Welfare, Health Resources Administration. *Project Summary: Board and Staff Composition of Health Planning Agencies.* Summary of "Assessment of Representation and Parity for HSAs and SHPDAs" study by Orkand Corporation, 1977.

U.S. Department of Health, Education and Welfare, Health Resources Administration. *The Consumer & Health Planning.* DHEW Publication No. HRA-77-14020. Washington, D.C.: Government Printing Office, 1977.

U.S. Department of Health, Education and Welfare, Health Services and Mental Health Administration. *Towards A Systematic Analysis of Health Care in the United States.* DHEW Publication No. HSM-73-25. Washington, D.C.: Government Printing Office, 1972.

U.S. Department of Health, Education and Welfare, National Council on Health Planning and Development, Subcommittee on Implementation and Administration. "Interim Report on Consumer Participation." March 1980.

U.S. Department of Health, Education and Welfare, National Institute of Mental Health. *Citizen Participation in Community Mental Health Centers, An Annotated Bibliography and Theoretical Models.* DHEW Publication No. ADM-79-737. Washington, D.C.: Government Printing Office, 1979.

U.S. Department of Health, Education and Welfare, National Institute of Mental Health. *Orientation Manual for Citizen Boards of Federally Funded Community Mental Health Centers.* DHEW Publication No. ADM-80-759. Washington, D.C.: Government Printing Office, 1980.

U.S. Department of Health, Education and Welfare, Public Health Service, Health Resources Administration, Bureau of Health Facilities, Financing, Compliance and Conversion. *1978--New Year for New Bureau, Annual Report Fiscal 1978.* DHEW Publication No. HRA-79-14505. Washington, D.C.: Government Printing Office, 1979.

U.S. Department of Health, Education and Welfare, Public
    Health Service, Health Resources Administration. *Health
    Planning in Action, Achieving Equal Access to Quality
    Health Care at a Reasonable Cost.* DHEW Publication No.
    HRA-80-14000. Washington, D.C.: Government Printing
    Office, 1980.

U.S. Department of Health, Education and Welfare, Public
    Health Service, Health Resources Administration. *Health
    Service Areas Designated Under the National Health
    Planning and Resources Development Act of 1974.* DHEW
    Publication No. HRA-78-14014. Washington, D.C.:
    Government Printing Office, 1978.

U.S. Department of Health, Education and Welfare, Public
    Health Service, Health Resources Administration, Office
    of Health Resources Opportunities. *A Focus on the
    Disadvantaged, Annual Report Fiscal 1979.* DHEW
    Publication No. HRA-80-608. Washington, D.C.: Govern-
    ment Printing Office, March 1980.

U.S. Department of Health, Education and Welfare, Public
    Health Service, Health Resources Administration, Office
    of Planning, Evaluation, and Legislation. *The
    National Guidelines for Health Planning, Standards
    Regarding the Appropriate Supply, Distribution and
    Organization of Health Resources.* DHEW Publication
    No. HRA-79-645. Washington, D.C.: Government Printing
    Office, 1979.

U.S. Department of Health, Education and Welfare, Public
    Health Service, Health Resources Administration. *The
    National Guidelines for Health Planning.* DHEW
    Publication No. HRA-79-645. Washington, D.C.: Govern-
    ment Printing Office, 1979.

U.S. Department of Health, Education and Welfare, Public
    Health Service. *Uncertainties of Federal Child Health
    Policies: Impact in Two States.* DHEW Publication No.
    PHS-78-3190. Washington, D.C.: Government Printing
    Office, 1978.

U.S. Department of Transportation. *Effective Citizen
    Participation in Transportation Planning.* Washington,
    D.C.: Government Printing Office, 1976.

Van De Water, Paul N. "Disability Insurance." *American
    Economic Association* 69(May 1979):275-278.

Van Til, J., and Van Til, S. B. "Citizen Participation
    in Social Policy: The End of the Cycle?" *Social
    Problems* 17(1970):313-323.

Vladeck, Bruce C. "The Design of Failure: Health Policy
    and the Structure of Federalism." *Journal of Health
    Politics, Policy and Law* 4(Fall 1979):522-535.

Wagner, Judith L. "Criteria for Project Review." *American Journal of Health Planning* 1(April 1977):11-16.

Walker, J. L. "The Diffusion of Innovations Among the States." *American Political Science Review* 63(1969): 867-869, 880-889.

Waters, William J. "Health Planning and National Health Insurance." *Inquiry* 15(September 1978):207-209.

Weber, M. *From Max Weber*. Edited by H. Gerth and C. W. Mills. New York: Oxford University Press, 1946.

Weiner, Stephen M. "Health Care Policy and Politics: Does the Past Tell Us Anything About the Future? *American Journal of Law and Medicine* 5(Winter 1980): 331-341.

Weinert, Bert. "Accountability in a Health Care System." *Consumer Health Perspectives* 5(October 1978):6-7.

West, Jonathan P. "Health Planning in Multifunctional Regional Councils: Baltimore and Houston Experience." *Inquiry* 12(September 1975):180-192.

West, Jonathan P., and Stevens, Michael D. "Comparative Analysis of Community Health Planning: Transition from CHPs to HSAs." *Journal of Health Politics, Policy and Law* 1(Summer 1976):173-195.

Western Center for Health Planning. *Educational Manual for HSA Volunteers*. San Francisco: Western Center for Health Planning, 1976.

Wright, Deil S. "Intergovernmental Relations: An Analytical Overview." *The Annals of the American Academy* 616(November 1974):1-16.

Wright, Deil S. "Intergovernmental Relations and Policy Choice." *Publius: The Journal of Federalism* 5(Fall 1975):1-24.

Wright, Deil S. *Understanding Intergovernmental Relations*. North Scituate: Duxbury Press, 1978.

Zald, M. N. "Political Economy: A Framework for Comparative Analysis." In *Power in Organizations*, pp. 221-261. Edited by M. N. Zald. Nashville: Vanderbilt University Press, 1970.

Zwick, Daniel I. "Health Planning: Past, Present and Future." *Health and Medical Care Services Review* 2(1979):1-15.

APPENDIX:
SPEAKERS AT PUBLIC HEARING
HELD ON MARCH 27, 1980, AND
AUTHORS OF WRITTEN STATEMENTS

SPEAKERS

BACON, BRENDA, Vice-President, Board of Directors,
    Southern New Jersey Health Systems Agency
BAD HAND, HOWARD, Program Analyst, National Indian Health
    Board, Inc.
CAIN, HARRY P., II, Executive Director, American Health
    Planning Association
CHAVKIN, DAVID, Managing Attorney, National Health Law
    Program
CLARKE, GARY, Director, Intergovernmental Health Policy
    Program, George Washington University
CURTIS, RICHARD, Associate Staff Director for Health
    Policy, Committee on Human Resources, National Gov-
    ernors' Association
EWING, MARGARET, Attorney, Mental Health Law Project
FEINSON, CLARE, Associate Director, Consumer Coalition
    for Health
GILBERT, RICHARD, Legislative Counsel, Office of Federal
    Relations, National League of Cities
HOWARD, PHYLLIS, Consumer Board Member, Central Indiana
    Health Systems Agency, Inc.
JACKSON, STEPHEN, Instructor, Tulane University
JOHNSON, EDDIE BERNICE, Chairperson, Task Force on Con-
    sumer Affairs, Health Services Administration
KNOX, JULIAN, Senior Service Fellow, Task Force on Con-
    sumer Affairs, Health Services Administration
McCARRON, DAVID, Coalition Staff Organizer, Cape Cod
    Health Care Coalition
MERRITT, RICHARD, Staff Director, Human Resources,
    National Conference of State Legislators
ROEPE, HAZEL ANN, Consumer Board Member, Hudson Valley
    Health Systems Agency, Inc.

123

YOUNGERMAN, ROBERT, Executive Director, North Central
  Georgia Health Systems Agency, Inc.

WRITTEN STATEMENTS

JARVIS, E. A., Board Member, Southeast Kansas Health
  Systems Agency
LADIMER, IRVING, Program Director, American Arbitration
  Association
LANG, GERALD S., Special Assistant for Policy, Office of
  the Assistant Chief Medical Director for Planning and
  Program Development, Veterans Administration
MACKIE, BERT, State Regent, Oklahoma State Regents for
  Higher Education
PERRINE, EDWARD L., Executive Director, Florida Gulf
  Health Systems Agency
SPARKS, ROBERT D., Michigan Department of Health, Public
  Health Advisory Council, Section 1122 Subcommittee
TIERNEY, JOHN, Associate Director, Health Planning and
  Resources Development, Rhode Island Department of
  Health